HF Radio E-Mail

For

"Idi-Yachts"®

A Guide For Setting Up and Using
Wireless E-Mail
Through Ham/Marine SSB Radio

By

Captain Marti Brown

PUBLISHED BY:

Cruising Companion Publications

P.O. Box 500441

Marathon, Florida 33050

E-Mail: captmarti@netzero.com

WEB: http://www.idiyachts.com

Cover page & CD ROM design: Brian Murphy at Digital Dreamland
WEB: http://digitaldreamland.org

M-802 Marine SSB front cover image courtesy of Icom America
Hurricane Floyd 09-14-99 back cover image courtesy of NOAA

ISBN 0-971-5640-1-9

Library of Congress Control Number: 2003094371

HF Radio E-Mail For "Idi-Yachts"®

By Captain Marti Brown

First Edition

Acknowledgments

I would like to acknowledge the following people for all of their wonderful assistance. Without their valued input this publication would not have been possible.

Ron Knaggs, N1GYX, Net Control for the AirMail/Winlink Tech Net who generously gave hundreds of hours of his time to edit and provide feedback on the numerous drafts that I sent him! Jim Corenman, KE6RK, author of AirMail and cofounder of The SailMail Association, Steve Waterman, K4CJX, system administrator and cofounder of WL2K, Vic Poor, W5SMM, Rick Muething, KN6KB, also cofounders and team members of Winlink 2000, Sam Ulbing N4UAU, Jim Johnston WB4GQK, Dave and Jan Wheeler, N0LSK & N0LTA, Betsy LeBlanc, M/V The Power of Two, Kathy Parsons for all of her wonderful mentoring, Carol and Dick Simmons, S/V Gusto, Ted Gimble, N1XVR, Steve Bowden and Pam House of Sea Tech Systems, Chuck Grey ND7K, Max Mayfield Director, National Hurricane Center, Tim Rulon National Weather Service, Christopher Burr, Chief, Tropical Analysis and Forecast Bureau, National Weather Service, Ray Williamson, N4JSR, Marathon RadioShack, Greg and Linda Henley, S/V Flirt, and Brian Murphy of Digital Dreamland and anyone I may have missed!

CONTENTS

The Purpose Of This Guide

I began experimenting with wireless HF radio E-Mail back in November of 1997 after I had set off alone on my sailboat to points unknown. In planning for my adventure, I realized that I needed a way to keep in touch with my family. They are all confirmed landlubbers and at the time were convinced I had lost my mind. I figured that my keeping in touch with them would either validate or dispute their notions about my mental status.

I purchased a KAM+ modem before I left port. Time was short and I didn't have a chance to use the modem before I left. Two weeks later I found myself anchored and weathered in at Boot Key Harbor, Marathon, in the Florida Keys. I struggled to figure out how to use the modem and became very frustrated. During a lull in the endless rain I took a ride in the dinghy. I noticed what looked like a HAM radio antenna on a sailboat nearby called "Patience." I decided that I could use a dose of that and so I knocked on their boat. I met Greg and Marilyn Moffitt, who were also trying to figure out how to use their KAM+ modem and having no luck with it. Together we spent numerous hours struggling with the modem and the terminal commands and got no where. In December, my new friends left to visit family in Canada for the holidays. When they returned they brought a new software program called AirMail that they had found on the Internet. We installed the program and after a few mistakes finally made our first connection! There was joy in the harbor that night for sure.

This guide is the product of a great deal of trial and error in learning how to set up a wireless HF radio E-Mail system. As I began mentoring folks on how to set up and use this system it became apparent that a guide on the subject might be useful to a large number of folks. The purpose of this book is to educate and promote effective wireless HF E-Mail set up, good radio practices, HF radio safety and to do so in such a way as to minimize frustration.

"Fair waves, both radio and ocean, and good E-mailing!"
Captain Marti Brown, KF4TRG
S/V The Other Woman

CHAPTER 1
INTRODUCTION

Wherever you are in the world you can keep in touch with loved ones or business associates by E-mail even if you do not have access to a telephone or

Figure 1.1
Icom M-802 Marine SSB
Courtesy of Icom America

to the Internet. Gone are the days when you had to dinghy off the boat when it was raining to find a phone to either hook up your lap top or to use for a Pocketmail download. No more need to wait for the "snail mail" connections in remote areas of the world where, "De mail boat only comes on Wednesdays, Mon."

This guide will help you set up a wireless HF radio E-mail system through a HAM and/or Marine SSB radio using a digital type radio modem. There are many other digital modes for sending and receiving radio E-mail that are available to the licensed HAM radio operator. If this piques your interest, see Appendix A for references and the enclosed "Idi-Yacht" CD ROM for information and software programs to get you started.

HAM radio and Marine SSB radio work essentially the same way. They just use different frequencies. So, from now on let's refer to both as HF radio–which stands for High Frequency. The text is written with the assumption that you the reader do not hold an engineering degree and probably have little, if any, training or knowledge in the field of electronics. To get you up and running, I'll start with some basic information such as a comparison of the features of HF Radio E-mail versus a Satellite phone and SSB receiver system, how the HF radio works, HF E-mail basics and the history of HF radio E-mail.

HF E-MAIL VS A SATELLITE PHONE

Many cruisers are finding themselves at the crossroads in deciding whether to equip their boats with a satellite phone for E-mail and a SSB RECEIVER for weather information or install an HF Radio TRANSCEIVER and HF radio E-mail system. The following is taken from E-mails I received from Vic Poor, the inventor of the microprocessor, Winlink 2000 and the technical consultant for the world's largest common carrier and from Jim Corenman, the author of the AirMail software program, where they express some basic reasons why you should not leave port without an HF TRANSCEIVER:

From Vic Poor, W5SMM:

"Sat phones are OK in their place but are of limited utility on a cruising yacht. You can use it to make rather expensive phone calls back home but it is a poor and costly way to communicate with fellow cruisers, summon help, send and receive E-mail, get the latest weather, make position reports, find your fellow cruisers, or get the latest world news. Yet with two-way HF radio you can do all of these things reliably, any time, and at no incremental cost. Some of these benefits only come when you have taken the trouble to obtain a general class ham license (something every long distance cruiser should do) but even without it HF radio offers the greater benefit.

Of course, every one that ventures offshore will carry an EPIRB (or better yet one of the new GPIRBs), a marine VHF radio, and a GPS receiver. There is no alternative to those essential items but after that a properly installed HF radio is next. The down side to HF radio is that it takes a little operating skill and care must be taken with the installation but these are nothing that any cruiser can't master."

From Jim Corenman, KE6RK:

"One of the great rewards of the cruising life style is the number of great folks that you will meet and get to know, folks from entirely different backgrounds who share the same dreams and goals as you. A few will become special friends, the kind of friends that you want to stay in touch with and would like to chat with in the morning over coffee, sharing experiences and planning the next reunion. With a SSB radio this is as simple as choosing a time and frequency, even when you are many hundreds of miles apart exploring different islands. Without a SSB radio, it will not happen. Using precious sat-phone minutes is simply not an option. So unless you are a true hermit, you WILL make new friends, and you WILL want to stay in touch with them as you wander through the anchorages. And if you don't install a SSB radio before you depart, then you WILL install one down the road a ways, someplace where doing so will be more expensive and a lot less convenient. So our advice is to save the money and aggravation, and do it before you depart." I wholeheartedly agree with both Vic and Jim.

Of course there are positive and negative features with both systems. A satellite phone and a SSB RECEIVER are fairly simple to set up and use. The HF radio TRANS-CEIVER and HF E-mail system requires the user to come up on a rather steep learning curve. Both systems require a significant financial investment. At first glance the purchase of a satellite phone and a SSB RECEIVER appears to be the cheaper way to go. Initially it is a little cheaper but not in the long run!

Set Up Costs

A Globalstar satellite phone with the E-mail cable kit costs about $650 plus a one time $50 set up fee and a monthly service plan.[1] For comparison let's use their $50 plan that buys you 120 prepaid minutes per month.[1] An Iridium satellite phone and E-mail system (the marine 9505 package) will cost you about $1650 plus a $50 activation fee and a monthly service plan.[1] For comparison let's use

---

1 - *Average retail prices as of September 2003, in US dollars*

HF RADIO E-MAIL FOR "IDI-YACHTS"®

their $93.99 a month service plan that buys you 60 prepaid minutes per month.[1] A SSB RECEIVER can cost up to $500[1]. So your set up costs for a Globalstar phone, E-mail kit and a SSB receiver would be approximately $1800.[1] For an Iridium phone, E-mail kit and a SSB receiver your set up costs would be $2828.[1]

A HAM/SSB E-mail system will cost you about $1800-$3000.[1] Commercial E-mail flat fees are about $200 a year.[1] Note that the cost of the Winlink HAM E-mail system is zero. Your set up costs for an HF radio E-mail system would be approximately $2600. This assumes that you bought the HF radio, tuner, and the HF radio modem for $2400 and paid for a $200 per year Commercial E-mail account.

Minutes Per Month & Overage Fees

With your 120 prepaid minutes plan using a Globalstar phone you would have about four minutes a day for phone calls and to access your E-mail. The sixty minutes per month plan using an Iridium phone would give you two minutes a day for phone calls and E-mail. Checking your E-mail or down-loading weather using a satellite phone can get really expensive considering that satellite phones are slow as molasses when it comes to data connections. Globalstar has a 9600 baud rate and Iridium has a whopping 4800. It is very likely that you would incur additional fees for going over your monthly plan limit. You could easily increase your yearly costs by $90[2] for Globalstar or $144[3] for Iridium with just ten minutes a month of overage! You might decide to add in a compression service to significantly boost your baud rate which will help keep the overage costs down. This would cost you an additional $20 per month or $216 per year.[4]

---

1 - Average retail prices as of September 2003, in US dollars
2 - Prices as of September 2003, US dollars based on $0.75 per minute charge
3 - Prices as of September 2003, US dollars based on $1.20 per minute charge
4 - Prices as of September 2003, US dollars for Global Marine Networks"XGATE"

HF radio E-mail is also a slow system but you can get more minutes to use on this system and pay a one time flat *yearly* fee. An HF radio E-mail Commercial account will buy you anywhere from ten minutes per day to 600 minutes per month depending upon which plan you select. Overage charges with HF radio E-mail are very rare if nonexistent.

Total Costs For First and Subsequent Years

Let's look at the total costs you could pay for the first year and for subsequent years with these systems. Including the equipment costs, the set up fee, the monthly minute plan, ten minutes per month of overage fees and the cost of data compression services, the Globalstar and SSB receiver option could cost you $2106 for the first year and $906 for each subsequent year. With all of the above fees an Iridium E-mail system and a SSB RECEIVER would run approximately $3188 in the first year and $1488 for each subsequent year. An HF radio E-mail system with a flat rate service provider would cost approximately $2600 for the first year and $200 for each subsequent year. In just three years you could save $1,000 to $3100 or more by selecting an HF radio E-mail system!

Emergency Communications

If your only option is a satellite phone for long distance communications and you have an emergency at sea, who are you going to call? You would probably first call the Coast Guard. The Coast Guard would try to figure out what ships might be located near you. They would then try and contact these ships *through their HF radio* and ask them to help you. Unless you have installed an external satellite antenna (which will cost more money) you will have to go out into the cockpit of your boat, clear of the bimini, to make your emergency call. If the wind is blowing 30 knots or higher you're going to have a lot of trouble hearing and making yourself heard on that satellite phone!

If you have an HF radio and put out a voice radio distress call, both the Coast Guard and ships in your immediate vicinity will hear your transmission and can render assistance. The Digital Selective Calling (DSC) option could also be used to send out a distress transmission if your radio has this feature. Both the Coast Guard and all ships at sea are required to monitor the DSC frequency. Your exact location and nature of distress would be transmitted automatically and continuously freeing you up to tend to the emergency at hand. This could save your life or the life of a loved one and that is priceless!

World Wide Coverage Issues

All areas of the world are not covered for voice and/or data connections with the Globalstar system as of this writing. Iridium is the only provider of worldwide satellite phone coverage. Even the Iridium system has some dead spots where there is no coverage. In contrast, you can make a phone call through your HF radio to or from anywhere in the world!

Finding Technical Assistance In Remote Areas

If you have a technical question about your engine or your watermaker who are you going to call? With a Satellite phone you can expect that a phone call to a technical support person for these items will cost you money and a fair amount of airtime. With Marine Single Sideband or HAM radio, knowledgeable help is available free of charge through the radio.

Cruising & Running A Business

If you plan on running a business that requires you to access the Internet in remote areas of the world, I would strongly recommend having an HF radio, an HF radio E-mail system *and* a satellite phone with a compression service. Use the satellite phone to briefly surf the Internet and use the HF radio to connect to your fellow cruisers and send your HF radio E-mail. See Appendix C for satellite phone compression services. Remember that there is also therapy for this addiction to the four letter word of "work" as well!

HOW HF RADIO WORKS

It's a good idea to have a general understanding of how HAM/Marine SSB radio works. Very simply put, the HF radio receives and transmits energy in the form of radio waves. When you press the button on the microphone and talk, the radio translates your voice into radio waves. These "waves" move out from the radio, move up through your antenna

Figure 1.2
Indirect Internet Connection

and up and out to space. Radio waves travel at the speed of light; 300,000,000 meters per second. Up in space, these waves are greeted by layers of ionized or charged gases. Similar to a mirror, these charged gases/particles reflect the radio waves back down to earth at different angles; hundreds and sometimes thousands of miles from where you've transmitted them. HF Radio waves can also hug the surface of the earth in a format called "Ground Wave" transmission. However, the long distance transmissions are a result of the reflection of the radio waves up in space. In a nutshell, that is how you get the long distance communications that are the hallmark of HF radio.

When you have a conversation on the HAM/Marine SSB radio it is very different from a telephone or a "land line." On a telephone you can talk and hear the other person talk at the same time. On a HAM/SSB radio one person talks and the other listens, and vice versa. If two people try to transmit or talk at the same time all that is heard is gobledeegook. This is a situation that is referred to as "doubling." This concept is an important one especially when you begin using HF radio E-mail.

HF E-MAIL BASICS

HF radio E-mail is an indirect connection to the Internet that uses a specialized HF radio E-mail provider. In other words, you will not be able to "surf the net" or access your E-mail directly. Using a computer, a software program, a radio modem (often called a Terminal Node Controller TNC), and an HF radio, you transmit your E-mail to an HF radio E-mail service provider

Computer

HF Radio

Modem

Figure 1.3
HF Radio E-mail Hardware
M-802 Radio Courtesy Icom America,
PTC-IIe Modem Courtesy of SCS

on specific frequencies that have been allocated for data transmissions. The HF radio E-mail service provider picks up your messages and stores them on their computer. At periodic times of the day or in some cases immediately, the service provider uploads your E-mail onto the Internet. E-mail that has been sent to you is downloaded from the Internet by the service provider and placed in a mailbox on the service provider's computer. When you connect to the service provider the messages in your mailbox are sent to you. See Figures 1.2 and 1.3.

To successfully use HF radio E-mail you will have to have an HF radio capable of sending these data transmissions. If you have a radio that is ten years old or more it might not be able to handle the rigors of HF radio E-mail transmissions. Check your manual or manufacturer for technical specifications (See Chapter 2 for more information). The radio modem translates the ones and zeros of computer language to analog or radio language and then tells the radio to transmit the translation. The type of HF radio modem that you need will use one of three data transmission modes or protocols called "Pactor." Pactor-1 is by far the slowest with a net data rate of approximately 200 bits per minute. Pactor-3 is the fastest protocol as of this writing with a net data rate of approximately 2800 bits per minute. Pactor-2 is the intermediate speed protocol with an approximate net data rate of up to 800 bits per minute. Real time operating speeds of Pactor protocols are affected by varying atmospheric conditions but they are robust and do keep the connection better than any other HF protocol, especially when used with the better modems. See the section on "Propagation" in Chapter 7 to learn more about factors that can adversely affect the speed of Pactor protocols.

The computer that you use must have enough memory and speed to handle the task of the HF radio E-mail software program. Each HF radio E-mail service provider uses a different software program. To run the software, you must have Windows 95 or higher on your computer. These computer requirements are addressed in Chapter 3. There are two types of HF radio E-mail providers; HAM and Commercial. The differences between the two and the requirements for using these two systems are discussed in Chapter 4.

HF radio E-mail is a one to one customer connection. You will need to learn to listen for some characteristic Pactor mode sounds and for other sounds that indicate that the frequency is in use. Check out the "Idi-Yacht" CD ROM to listen to these sounds of Pactor mode transmissions and digital transmissions. If you do transmit and the frequency is busy you could cause the poor soul who is connected to be disconnected. That's not good Karma!

HF RADIO E-MAIL HISTORY

E-mail sent through an HF radio is simply digital or data transmissions/reception as opposed to voice transmissions/reception. The first form of digital transmissions were Morse code. In Morse code each letter or number consists of a series of short and long signal pulses in the form of dots and dashes respectively. The shorter "dits" and longer "dahs" are combined into strings that communicate the entire alphabet and numbers. Samuel Morse invented this technology in 1894. He was an artist that wanted to keep in touch with his family during long sea voyages from Europe. Ships at sea began voluntarily using his technology for distress and safety communications in 1895. After the sinking of the Titanic in 1912, the US government required all ships at sea to have and monitor Morse

Figure 1.4
GN507b Morse Keyer
Courtesy Morse Express & Oak Hill Research

code. Its use aboard seafaring vessels required the shipping companies to dedicate trained operators to spend long hours monitoring the emergency frequencies. Morse code transmissions are no longer monitored by ships at sea or by the Coast Guard.

Next a machine that could automatically send, receive and print digital signals automatically called Radioteletype (RTTY) was invented. A new code called Baudot was developed to establish a digital language for Radioteletype data transmissions and reception. Unlike Morse code, these data bits are sent by shifting frequencies--Frequency Shift Keying (FSK). By putting together combinations of the mark and space signals the operator can send letters, numbers and some limited punctuation marks. Individual characters are separated by start and stop signals.

When data are sent over long distances on the HF frequencies there is a tendency for increased noise and subsequent fading of the signal to occur. When this happens the receiving station does not get all of the message. This is one of the major handicaps of both the Morse code and RTTY systems.

SITOR and AMTOR systems were developed to minimize this problem of signal fading and noise in data transmissions by using an automated error checking system. SITOR (SImplex Teletype Over Radio) was developed commercially for the Maritime Mobile Service. AMTOR (Amateur Teletype Over Radio) was developed for use by HAM radio operators. The receiving station automatically detects erroneous or garbled data when it does not receive a four mark and three bit character and then automatically requests a repeat of the data from the sending station. So, if part of the sending station's transmission is garbled or faded due to a static crash or atmospheric noise, the receiving station automatically requests a repeat of the data. This automated technology is referred to as ARQ which is short for Automatic Repeat reQuest. When the data or signal is repeated, the odds are that the repeated signal or data will be received more clearly the second (or more) time around. Can you imagine having to do all of that manually?

In early 1980 HAMs began experimenting with linking AMTOR transmissions and Amateur Packet radio networks. Amateur Packet transmissions are communications over HAM radio between two computers. Packet networks use relays and stations that act as bulletin boards for message storage, retrieval and forwarding. The development of "APlink" by Vic Poor, W5SMM allowed messages sent from long distances on HF radio using AMTOR to be linked to local Packet radio nets. This software was run in a DOS operating system. Remember DOS? It's also known as a Difficult Operating System!

In 1985 Microsoft Windows version 1.0 was released. This system provided a more user friendly computer operating platform. Vic upgraded his APlink program to work within the Windows operating system and called the program Winlink Classic.

HF RADIO E-MAIL FOR "IDI-YACHTS"®

In 1994 Hans Kessler, N8PGR, took ownership of Winlink Classic. He wrote numerous enhancements to it including a very  robust new mode called CLO-VER. About the time that Winlink Classic was being introduced, Pactor-1 technology was developed by a group of Hams in Germany who formed the Special Communication Systems (SCS) company. The Pactor system combines features from both AMTOR and Packet systems. Similar to AMTOR, it sends blocks of characters and uses ARQ (that error checking system). They were first to improve upon ARQ with the development of an analog memory error correction system. This allows a modem using the Pactor protocol to try and reconstruct a good block of data out of several bad or partially received blocks of data. SCS went on to develop Pactor-2 which includes the analog memory ARQ of Pactor-1 as well as a powerful Digital Signal Processing (DSP) chip and an incorporated 32 bit microprocessor. A DSP chip provides high quality data compression to help speed things along.

As Internet E-mail grew in popularity, operators of the Winlink Classic system began to experiment with uploading HF radio messages onto the Internet. Steve Waterman, K4CJX, knew that before long, conventional HAM to HAM digital communications were going to die a slow death. This sparked the idea to connect the Winlink radio messaging system into the Internet E-mail system. After getting much positive confirmation from others, Steve spent over a year looking for a programmer to make it happen. Finally, Jim Jennings, W5EUT, agreed to research how to accomplish the Internet interface with Winlink. Jim soon came up with "Netlink" which allowed HF radio E-mail to be transferred to the Internet. Steve and Jim tested and refined the system and Steve gathered others who would offer this service. Jim and Hans added further enhancements to Winlink/Netlink that allowed it to automatically generate weather bulletins based on text based WEB data.

One of the first users of this system was Rick Muething, KN6KB. While he sailed from San Francisco to Melbourne, Florida, Rick sent and received HAM radio E-mail messages through Steve's station. When the Internet link was completed he became hooked on the system and one of the first Netlink stations.

The AirMail software program was developed by Jim Corenman, KE6RK. Jim is a HAM radio operator, a cruising sailor and a retired electronics and computer engineer. He has worked with AMTOR and APlink stations since 1993. While cruising in the South Pacific on his sailboat *Heart of Gold*, he became acutely aware of the need for an Internet transfer of HF radio E-mail messages. His APlink messages would often take about a week to be delivered from his remote location. Sometimes they would get lost and wouldn't be delivered at all! He also saw the need for a software program that would provide an E-mail style message window and that would simplify the special formatting that was required to connect to the Netlink stations. At that time the Pactor user was forced to learn and use a sort of secret code to connect to the Netlink stations. Those of us without any computer programming experience paled at the technical learning curve. Many long and frustrating hours were spent trying to read and decipher obscure and confusing technical HF modem manuals.

In the fall of 1997 he released the first version of AirMail. HAM radio operators on cruising boats, recreational vehicles, missionaries, medical relief programs and HAMs living in remote areas of the world soon discovered this easy to use program. The number of users connecting to the Netlink stations increased dramatically.

In 1998 Steve, Rick, Hans and Vic met in Cleveland, Ohio to refine the Winlink/Netlink system and to design what is now called the Winlink 2000 system (WL2K). They envisioned a "feature rich" program that would also be user friendly for the volunteer network stations. This system was implemented in February of 1999 and today it is the undisputed largest and most sophisticated wireless HF E-mail system in the world. WL2K now offers over 700 weather and help bulletins through the AirMail client software. The system allows the user to access weather products and E-mail through any of the participating WL2K network stations. Position reports can be sent and vessel locations can be accessed from the Internet. Weather reports from ships at sea can be forwarded to meteorologists to assist them in forecasting. Users can now retrieve their HF radio E-mail directly through an Internet connection should they be away from the radio. They now have over 36 WL2K stations worldwide that process over 150,000 messages each month from 4300 users. AirMail continues to be the state-of-the art client program for WL2K.

Late in 1997 Stan Honey, WA6IVA, approached Jim Corenman about putting together a commercial E-mail service using Marine SSB frequencies. This service would be used to handle communications that were not possible on the HAM frequencies (business related) and by people that were not HAM radio operators. In March of 1998 they put up their first station and the Sail-Mail Association was born.

Pactor-3 has recently been developed by SCS. Both speed and efficiency have again been significantly increased. A Pactor-3 system is simply a Pactor-2 modem with a $150 software upgrade. As of this writing, the SCS company holds the patent on both Pactor-2 & 3 technology. In other words, if you want to get a Pactor-2 or a 3 modem the SCS PTC II, IIe, IIex or Pro modems are your only options. See Chapter 2 for more information.

Digital radio transmissions have certainly come a long way from the early days of Morse code and the RTTY, SITOR, AMTOR and APlink modes. With all of the improvements it is important to note that data transmissions through the Pactor mode are still at a snail's pace when compared to a DSL or a Broadband connection. Those of you that have become accustomed to high speed Internet E-mail access will have to work on your island time state of mind!

CHAPTER 2
HF E-MAIL EQUIPMENT

This chapter will help you assess and collect the additional items you will need in order to set up your HF radio E-mail system. Whether you already have an HF radio or are contemplating the purchase of one, the author recommends that you scrutinize your equipment to be sure that it can be used with Pactor mode HF radio E-mail. I'll review the requirements for the HF radio, the computer and discuss the different brands of HF radio modems that you have to choose from.

HF RADIO REQUIREMENTS

Your HF radio (HAM or Marine SSB) must be capable of continuous duty. What that means is that the radio has to be

Figure 2.1
Icom M-710 Marine SSB
Courtesy of Icom America

capable of transmitting continuously for about a minute or two without overheating. If your radio is six years or older it is probably not going to be able to withstand the rigors of HF radio E-mail and will probably overheat and shut down. Older radios can't switch back and forth from transmit to receive fast enough to operate modern digital protocols like Pactor. Some newer HF radios can't cut the mustard and require the addition of an oven fan to keep them cool. Check the manufacturer's information about the radio you intend to buy (or the one you own) carefully to be sure it meets these specifications.

The HF radio must be capable of operating on the frequencies that are set aside for data (E-mail) transmissions. All HAM radios are ready out of the box for HAM data frequencies. Most Marine SSB radios are capable of transmitting on these frequencies but must be programed or "opened" to do so. The reason for this is that Marine SSB radios are "highly channelized." That is to say they are designed to work on specific frequencies.

To ensure that they do work on these preset frequencies and avoid user error, many Marine SSB radios force the user to dial in a preprogramed ITU (International Telegraph Union) channel that will input the corresponding frequencies. The Marine SSB E-mail frequencies are often not preprogramed with these ITU data channels in both the older and the newer models. So, if you have a Marine SSB radio, you will have to determine whether or not it is "open" to programing these E-mail ITU channels so that you can access the HF radio E-mail Service provider that you select.

Consult your manual for information on how to program these channels or contact the manufacturer. If you are purchasing a brand spanking new Marine SSB radio, check with the distributor to be sure that the radio can access all of the HF radio E-mail frequencies. Better yet, have them program these channels for you.

There are a variety of HF radios to select from. Buyer beware. Not all HF radios can support prolonged transmissions and rapid switching from transmit to receive that E-mail modems require. Additionally, some Marine SSB radios are designed to receive only and not transmit on the HAM bands. If you are purchasing a radio be sure that the unit can both receive and transmit on the HAM bands as well as the Marine SSB bands especially if you plan to become a licensed HAM and use the HAM radio E-mail system. If you plan on dual use with both HAM and Marine SSB your options are to purchase a type accepted dual use radio or have two separate radios; a Marine SSB and a HAM radio.

Most Marine SSB radios cannot control their power output; they are limited to either a high or low power setting. This can have some ramifications regarding connecting to a service provider and courtesy issues when using HF radio E-mail in crowded anchorages. HAM radios can be adjusted to transmit on a wide variety of power settings. Both Marine SSB and HAM radios can be modified to transmit on HAM or Marine SSB frequencies. In the US there are legality issues to modifying an HF radio. If you are in the jurisdiction of the USA and not in International waters or operating under the rules of another country and you modify your HAM radio for use on the Marine frequencies or vice versa, you will risk fines from the FCC if you transmit on frequencies that have not been approved for your particular radio.

You must be licensed to transmit on the HAM radio frequencies and hold at least a General Class Amateur Radio license to use wireless HF radio E-mail and to participate in the HAM maritime nets. No license is required for the HAM bands if you listen only or unless you have a life threatening emergency. If you have a life threatening emergency you may then transmit on any frequency to get help.

Types of E-mail Ready HF Radios

It is critical that you select a radio that will provide you with the features that you need to successfully use HF radio E-mail. These radios are sometimes advertised as "E-mail Ready." On the next page, I'll list some of the HF radios that are E-mail ready, whether they can be used for dual HAM and Marine SSB operation, their average retail prices in US dollars and a few of their additional features.

HF Radio Cost Comparison Chart

RADIO[1]	TYPE	PRICE[2]	WATTS	OTHER[3]
ICOM M-802	Dual	$1899	150	DSC,R,RH
ICOM M-710 v2	Dual	$1599	150	R
ICOM M-700Pro	Marine	$1199	150	R
ICOM 706-MKIIG	HAM	$795	100	RH
ICOM IC-718	HAM	$599	100	R
ICOM IC-746 Pro	HAM	$1300	100	R
Kenwood TS-570DG	HAM	$700	100	R
Kenwood TS-2000	HAM	$1600	100	RH

1 = Requires an antenna and a tuner. See Chapter 3.
2 = Average retail prices as of September 2003, in US dollars.
3 = DSC- Digital Selective Calling (Only available with M-802).
    R-Remote computer control available.
    RH-Remote head option available (Standard with M-802).

COMPUTER REQUIREMENTS

You need to know how to operate a computer using Windows software. If you have never before used a computer it is imperative that you get some experience and knowledge on how to navigate through the software system. There are several books available that can help bring you up to speed. See Appendix A for more information.

Computer Operating System

The computer must have adequate memory; both Random Access Memory (RAM) and hard drive space. You will need at least 8 megabytes of RAM and 50 or more megabytes of free hard drive space. If you plan to run other programs at the same time along with the HF E-mail software program then count on having at least 16 to 32 megabytes of RAM. The more RAM you have, the faster your programs open and work. When you open a program, the computer grabs the program data and stores it in RAM. It's like having a big shopping cart to take groceries to your car. With a small cart, you need to make several trips back and forth to get all the groceries.

Microsoft Windows

All HF radio E-mail service providers require a Windows operating system. Check to see what version of Microsoft Windows you have on your computer. The Windows operating systems that are compatible with HF radio E-mail provider software include Windows 95, 98, ME, 2000 and XP.

For the best results it's important to have the most up to date operating system before you download and install any HF radio E-mail service provider's software. Even if you have a brand spanking new computer there are critical updates that won't be installed on the operating system.

For Windows software upgrades, log on to the Internet and go to http://www.microsoft.com. Follow the instructions for your particular operating system and download the necessary upgrades.

Macintosh

To use a Macintosh system you will have to install a Windows emulator program and run the service provider's software through the Windows emulator. You will also have to configure the COM port that you plan to use with the HF radio E-mail program through the Windows emulator program. Check with your service provider for some coaching on how to do this. A excellent WEB site with all sorts of information on using Windows emulators can be found at: http://www.macwindows.com.

Computer Serial Port Connections

The computer should have a serial port capable of connecting a 9 pin RS232 cable. See Figure 2.2 for an

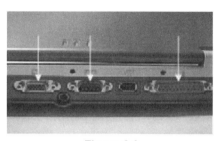

Figure 2.2
Computer Serial Ports

example of what serial ports look like on the back of my laptop. Take a look at the back of your computer. There should be a large female plug with 25 openings--that's your printer port. There should be two small ports, one with 15 holes and the other with 9 pins also somewhere in the back of your computer. The one with the nine male pins is the one you want for the HF modem to computer connection. If you are shopping for a computer, be sure to look carefully for this serial port. You'll need a shielded 9 pin RS232 cable that has one end with nine holes to plug into your computer and the other end with nine pins to plug into the back of your HF modem. I'll discuss radio and modem connections in Chapter 5.

Several lap top manufacturers have done away with the serial port and replaced it with USB ports. See Figure 2.3 for an example of what a USB port looks like on my computer. Don't despair however, as there are modifications that you can buy to make the connection. What you will need to buy is a USB to

Figure 2.3 USB Ports

Serial port converter and install the software for this device. See Chapter 5 for more information on USB to Serial

Port Converters. Refer to Appendix C "USB to Serial Port Converters" and Marine SSB Systems and Modems" for sources of this item. Please note that not all USB to Serial Port Converters will work. The vendors in Appendix C have the ones that are tried and true!

Additional Computer Considerations

Any brand or off brand of computer will work with HF radio E-mail. Before purchasing a new computer, test it to be sure that it does not generate noise that can interfere with the radio. Bring an AM/FM radio to the store with you. Turn it on to an AM station that has a crystal clear signal and move it close to the computer. If the radio station's signal becomes fuzzy or crackles with static then don't buy that computer! It will generate noise and interfere with your HF radio E-mail. Or plan to use it at least six feet from the radio and the HF radio modem.

HF RADIO MODEMS

There are many varieties of radio modems on the market. Whatever brand you select be sure that it is an HF Pactor mode radio modem. Buyer beware! There are some TNCs that are designed exclusively for VHF packet mode which is basically for the 2 meter HAM frequencies. Others are designed for HAM packet mode and Pactor-1. Some radio modem marketing materials refer to their Pactor-1 modem as a

Figure 2.4 SCS PTC-llex
Courtesy of SCS GmbH & Co.

"2." They really should say something like, "Pactor Too or Also." Remember, the only Pactor-2 modem on the market is made by SCS. In the following section, I'll review the types of HF Pactor modems, compare costs, give you some tips on how to select an HF radio modem and outline some of the other operating modes that are available on the HF radio modems.

Types of HF Radio Modems

You learned earlier that the Pactor mode HF radio modem is used for HF radio E-mail. The basic difference between Pactor-1, 2, and 3 is the speed of data; both transmission and reception. Pactor-1 is the slowest operating mode and Pactor-3 is the fastest. Accordingly, Pactor-1 is the cheapest and Pactor-3 is the most expensive. As of this writing, Pactor-3 mode is accomplished by purchasing a Pactor-2 modem (either a SCS PTC-II, PTC-IIe, PTC-IIex or PTC-II Pro) and a $150 software upgrade package. The modem becomes a Pactor-3 after you upgrade it with the software upgrade program. You'll also see this software upgrade referred to as a "professional firmware" upgrade. Most HF radio and modem distributors can sell you an HF modem that has already been upgraded. See Chapter 6 for more information on how to upgrade the modem to Pactor-3 and Appendix C for modem distributors and Pactor-3 upgrade sources.

HF Modem Cost Comparison Chart

MODEM	COMPANY	MODES	PRICE*
PTC-II	SCS	P1,2,3	USED[1,2,3]
PTC-IIe	SCS	P1,2,3	USED[1,3]
PTC-IIex	SCS	P1,2,3	$699[3]
PTC-IIPro	SCS	P1,2,3	$1049[3]

1 - Used equipment only. No longer manufactured.
2 - Pactor-3 Add $99 (USD) for Electronic Serial Number.
3 - Pactor-3 add $150 (USD) for the software upgrade.
* - Prices as of September 2003 in US dollars (USD).

SELECTING AN HF MODEM

The HF radio modem that will be right for you will depend upon your budget, your anticipated uses of HF radio E-mail and how rapidly technology changes. Pactor-1 mode is being discontinued and replaced by the Pactor-2 and 3 modes. It is just too slow and is clogging up

Figure 2.5
PTC-II Pro Pactor-2
Courtesy of SCS GmbH & Co.

the HF radio E-mail providers' systems. If your budget forces you to invest in a Pactor-1 modem then I recommend that you try and find a used KAM Plus or a PK232 Pactor-1 modem on Ebay and spend no more than $100 US for it! But be aware of Radio Frequency Interference (RFI) problems when using these older modems. They are not recommended for serious offshore communications.

Pactor-2 speeds can be up to six times faster than Pactor-1 with an average speed of four times faster. If you plan on downloading large data files such as GRIB Weather

Figure 2.6
SCS PTC-IIe Pactor-2
Courtesy of SCS GmbH & Co.

files see Chapter 8 for information on GRIB Weather files), business spread sheets, pictures, articles or book chapters you should purchase a Pactor-3 modem. The speed of a Pactor-3 modem is about 5 times faster than Pactor-2. The operating speed of Pactor-3 will help you use less time on the system and use less battery power.

Those of you that have owned a computer for the last five years are aware how quickly technology is updated. If you plan to cruise to remote areas of the world and be gone for a year or two and plan to download GRIB weather files and attachments, then I'd highly recommend that you spend the money and buy top of the line technology. Many of the HF radio E-mail Service Providers are moving to Pactor-2 as a minimum mode. You wouldn't want to be in Bora Bora looking to buy a new HF radio modem or to upgrade your system!

Other HF Modem Operating Modes

There are many other types of data communications that are available through an HF radio modem besides the Pactor mode. For licensed HAMs there is AMTOR, HF & VHF Packet, RTTY, CW, SSTV, FAX, and APRS and others. If any of these tweak your interest then see Appendix A and/or the "Idi-Yacht" CD ROM for more information on these modes.

For all users there is SITOR, RTTY, NAVTEX, and Weather Fax. NAVTEX and Weather Fax are free to view once you have the appropriate hardware or software. See Chapter 8 for more information. SITOR & RTTY services have a fee for service and also require special software. Please refer to Appendix A and/or the "Idi-Yacht" CD ROM for more information on these modes.

CHAPTER 3
HF RADIO SET UP

If you are preparing to install an HF radio or need to troubleshoot your rig, refer to Appendix A and the "Idi-Yacht" CD ROM for some good resources on configuring antennas, groundplanes, recommended size

Figure 3.1
Icom M-700Pro Marine SSB
Courtesy of Icom America

of wire based on the distance from the radio to the battery and the like. The proper set up of your HF radio will be crucial to maximizing it's capabilities in voice transmissions and in your success with HF radio E-mail. If you have any weak spots or poor installation techniques in your HF radio system you will have great difficulty using HF radio E-mail. First things first. Be sure that you've got the bugs out of your HF radio installation before you add more complexity to your system. In this chapter I'll discuss the components of an HF radio system, some sources of noise that could interfere with HF E-mail, RF isolation, and HF radio safety.

THE HF RADIO SYSTEM

The HF Radio

The HF radio should be located in a dry, splash proof area close to the navigation station or a table. It must be securely fastened to prevent any movement especially in boats, cars or Recreational Vehicle (RV) installations. The parts of an HF radio system include the transceiver which is powered by DC or battery current, a tuner/coupler, an antenna, and a groundplane.

DC Power Supply To the HF Radio

You must install the proper diameter wire for the length of the run. The length of the run from the radio includes both the positive and negative wire lengths. So, if your radio is six feet from the battery your total run length will be twelve feet. Got it? You can look up recommended wire sizes in tables based on the total length of the run. These tables will recommend wire size based upon the length of the run to the battery to help you minimize voltage drop or loss. Too small a wire diameter will cause more voltage loss and subsequently less power will be supplied to the radio. The less power or voltage you have going to the radio, the weaker your signal.

Don't forget to put the radio on a circuit breaker and install in-line fuses on both the positive and the negative wires close to the battery. Most manufacturers recommend a 30 amp fuse. Where possible, dedicate a battery to the HF radio or try to keep other connections on the HF radio battery to a minimum. This will go a long way in reducing electronic noise that can interfere with your HF Radio E-mail system. Consult your manual and see Appendix A for references on electrical wiring.

The HF Radio Tuner/Coupler

When you turn on the radio and initially key the microphone to transmit on a frequency you will need to tune the antenna. Tuning the antenna essentially helps you get the most powerful radio transmissions possible by matching the antenna with the frequency you've selected. Tuning can be accomplished in one of two ways; with an automatic tuner or a manual tuner. Tuners used to be referred to as "couplers." For the purposes of this guide I'll refer to them as tuners.

Automatic tuners are expensive but do afford the operator with a quick and easy way of getting the radio frequency and the antenna matched up and tuned. See Fig-

Figure 3.2
Icom AT-140 Tuner
Courtesy of Icom America

ures 3.2 and 3.3. Prices as of September 2003 for the Icom AT-130 and the AT-140 averaged around $429 and $459 respectively and the SGC tuner averaged around $499.[1] You will often find HF radio and automatic tuners bundled together for a one price packaged deal. Manual tuners are inexpensive but require that you make adjustments whenever you turn on the radio or change to a different frequency. Both the automatic and the manual tuners are connected in between the radio and the antenna. You should generally install the tuner as close

to the antenna as possible. If your installation is on a boat a car or a RV, I'd highly recommend that you purchase an automatic tuner. A manual tuner on a boat or RV is almost impossible to install close to the antenna. The further away the tuner is from the antenna, the more Radio Frequency Interference (RFI) will be generated.

Figure 3.3
SGC SG-230 Smartuner™
Courtesy of SGC

The tuner should also be installed in a dry location. Several of the automatic tuners are rated as "waterproof." However, the harsh salt water environment can quickly corrode the connections to the tuner which will result in a loss of power in your transmissions. Installing the automatic tuner in a protected location will go a long way in reducing corrosion and in avoiding any possibility of getting water inside the "waterproof" casing and destroying the sensitive electronic components.

---

1 - Average retail prices as of September 2003 in US dollars

If you have a Marine SSB radio and install an automatic tuner, please be sure that you set the tuning function to work only when you push the microphone to transmit and talk. This is generally a setting done within the HF radio. Set it to Push To Talk (PTT) tune and not to automatic tune. The "Automatic Tune Function" puts a nasty high pitched tone or carrier on the frequency as soon as you dial in the frequency. The tuner takes a few only a few milliseconds to tune when you key the microphone and talk. It seems to take forever to tune with the automatic tune feature.

If you use a manual tuner, please remember to always find a vacant frequency when you tune up. You should spend some time listening to be sure the frequency is not occupied. If you're tuning on a voice frequency and aren't sure if it's unoccupied, just ask! This noise can interfere with folks that are trying to talk on the frequency. It's about as obnoxious as someone blowing a loud high pitched whistle in your ear or the sound of fingernails screeching on a chalk board. Check out Appendix C for more information on sources of automatic and manual tuners.

The HF Radio Groundplane

Simply put, the job of a groundplane is to reflect radio waves up towards space. The groundplane (also called

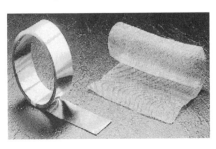

counterpoise) when it's installed correctly acts like a trampoline to send radio waves soaring into space. You must have a good groundplane attached to the antenna tuner. The ability of a groundplane to reflect radio waves depends upon

Figure 3.4
Copper Strap & Mesh
Courtesy of Newmar Corporation

28

the amount of surface area used in the installation. On a fiberglass boat a groundplane is made by using copper strap or mesh that is connected to the tuner. Most experts recommend using 100 square feet of 4-6" wide and about 0.13 inches thick copper strap (not the 0.001 inch thin foil!) to make this connection. Wire should never be used in a groundplane installation as it does not provide adequate surface area.

While you are installing the copper strap feel free to attach it to anything metal such as the fuel and water tanks, the hot water heater, a Dynaplate® or the Wonder Bar®, your through-hulls and/or your keel. (Note that tying in bonded through-hulls that are part of a lightening protection system is controversial.) By attaching these conductive metal structures to the copper strap you increase the surface area of your groundplane. The larger the surface area of the groundplane the stronger your signal!

If you are building a boat, have the manufacturer lay in 100 square feet of copper mesh in the hull that you can connect to the tuner with copper strap. Please note that this is not meant to be a comprehensive discussion regarding groundplanes. For more information refer to Appendix A or see Appendix C to consult a marine electronics expert.

The HF Radio Antenna

The antenna should be located as far away from the radio as possible. There are several options for installing an HF radio antenna on a boat. On a sailboat, the easiest and most efficient would be to put two antenna isolators on the backstay. The top isolator should be about four feet from the top of the mast. The lower isolator can be brought down close to the backstay turn-

Figure 3.5
Sta-Lok® Antenna Isolator
Courtesy of Sta-lok Terminals, Ltd.

buckle that fastens to the deck or hull. The length of the

backstay antenna (the space between the two antenna isolators) should be at least 9 feet long. Note that the longer the length of the antenna the better! A twenty-three to forty foot antenna will make it easier on the tuner to match a wide variety of frequencies. Check your tuner manual for brand specific instructions.

Wherever you install the antenna be sure that it cannot be touched by human hands or pets during transmission as severe burns will result. See the section on "Safety" in this Chapter for more discussion on this topic. The major downside to a standing rigging installation is that in the event you would experience a dismasting then you would lose your antenna.

A standard 17 or 23 foot Marine SSB antenna can be used for boats that don't have a backstay such as a powerboat and some of the new catamarans or for sailors concerned about dismasting. The sheer size of this antenna can be problematic for mounting but it is often the only alternative for some boats. Avoid buying antennas that are smaller than 17 feet as you will not be able to access all of the radio frequencies with these smaller antennas. See Appendix A for more information regarding the various antenna systems you can install on a boat. If you are interested in installing a whip antenna or would like some good information on automatic antenna tuners take a look at Jim Johnston's article in "Southwinds Magazine" also located in the Antenna section of Appendix A.

Figure 3.6
Galaxy SSB Antenna
Courtesy of Shakespeare

The antenna tuner is attached to the antenna using a special type of feed wire called GTO-15. The GTO is connected to the tuner using a ring terminal. Remove about 3 inches of insulation from the other end of the GTO and wrap it around the standing rigging immediately above the lower isolator. Secure the bare GTO using a stainless steel hose clamp. Wrap and seal the hose clamp and GTO with rigging or friction tape. That will help keep moisture and salt water from corroding the connection.

You should make the run from the antenna tuner to the antenna as short as possible. Plan to install the antenna tuner as close as you can to the antenna. Also note that the GTO feed wire becomes a part of the antenna so be sure that no metal objects or electrical wires come in contact with it as well. If possible, the GTO wire should run vertically (relative to the ground plane) as it is attached from the tuner to the connection point at the antenna.

Be sure to check for corrosion and clean the GTO to antenna connection and the GTO to tuner connection at least twice a year. More often than not problems with HF radios are a result of corrosion at these two points that causes an increase in resistance or Standing Wave Ratio (SWR). An ounce of prevention could well be worth a pound of cure!

Common Installation Mistakes

Several common "sins" of HF radio installation that I and others have seen and been guilty of include; an inadequate groundplane–skimping on copper or using the thin foil, DC power wires that are too small for the length of the run from the radio to the battery, using regular stranded wire to connect the backstay antenna to the tuner (instead of GTO 15 wire), corrosion on the antenna feed connection and/or the tuner connection, anything metal—such as a shroud cleat or a flag with metal clips—connected to the section of the backstay used for the antenna (that was one of my early mistakes) and incorrect antenna tuner installation. See Appendix A or the "Idi-Yacht" CD ROM for more references on HF radio installation.

SOURCES OF NOISE

Electronics such as autopilots, refrigerators, inverters, solar panels, wind generators, pumps and alternators can cause noise and interfere with your radio transmissions and reception. Some computers can generate a high level of noise. When you use HF radio E-mail you will need a noise free environment to be successful.

You will have to find sources of electrical noise and squelch them. My refrigerator compressor squeals, squeaks and beeps through my HF radio so loud that it is impossible for me to connect and receive HF E-mail. So much for high tech refrigerators. The problem with my fridge is in the compressor. If you are looking at refrigerators, I'd highly suggest that you take an AM radio with you, tune in a crystal clear station, have the vendor start up the refrigerator and listen. If the station crackles with static and you can't hear the music then don't buy that fridge! See the "Idi-Yacht" CD ROM for an example of the noises that you will be listening for.

There are DC noise filters available that you can attach to noisy electronics. Coiling the insulated section of the positive and negative DC wires with about five turns can help squelch noise that tries to travel through these wires--called a poor person's choke. Note that you should *never* coil coax or GTO feed wire. Check out Appendix C for equipment sources and Appendix A for references on troubleshooting noise. Sometimes the best you can do is determine which electronic devices are the offending culprits and just turn them off when you are using HF radio E-mail.

The reason why electronics on RVs and boats are so noisy is that the FCC exempts devices that will be used on boats, RVs and cars but mandates RFI standards on electronics used in the home. This is FCC Rule 15 Part B. Complain to the FCC and maybe sometime in the future we will have less noise to squelch!

RF ISOLATION

When you transmit on an HF radio, radio waves are generated by the transceiver. If all is working properly, these waves move from the radio, through the tuner, up the an-

Figure 3.7
RF Chokes

tenna and out into space. Radio waves or radio frequencies (RF) are similar to water in that they will travel the path of least resistance. These waves must be discouraged from wandering towards other paths that might be easier to flow to for two reasons. First, you want to try and get all of the transmitted radio waves through and out of the antenna rocketing towards space. Radio waves that don't get up into space aren't going to get you any distance in your communications. Second, wandering RF can migrate back to the HF radio creating noise, distortion and all kinds of trouble especially with HF radio E-mail. So how do you make the path to space the most attractive one and discourage wandering? Go out and buy a good quantity of RF chokes which are also known as ferrite beads or toroids. See Fig-

Figure 3.8
Clip-On RF Chokes

ure 3.8. These marvels of modern science make the alternate paths less attractive and are available in many sizes and shapes. To be effective, the RF choke must fit snugly over the cable or wire.

RF can try and sneak back to the transceiver and/or the HF radio modem through the outside of the cable shield. Attaching the RF chokes over this cable at both ends near the plugs will make those rascal stray waves think twice about wandering. Additionally, several clip-on RF chokes

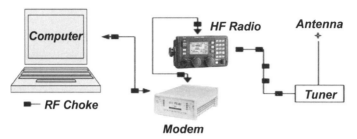

Figure 3.9 RF Choke Placement
M-802 Courtesy of Icom America,
PTC II-ex Courtesy SCS GmbH & Co.

placed over the coax cable that connects the transceiver to the tuner are also recommended. See Figure 3.9. Some folks even recommend an RF choke clipped over the insulated section of the power wire to the radio.

So now you've got your RF moving on the right path and those deviant waves that might have had a fleeting thought about wandering to new and uncharted territory are all choked up and headed towards outer space! The size of the clip-on RF choke that will fit most cables is the one with a 1/4 inch hole. Take some measurements to be sure you get a snug fit. RF chokes can be purchased at Radio Shack, most HAM radio stores, HAM festivals and of course on the Internet. See Appendix C for a list of RF choke vendors.

Many installers and HF radio E-mail providers also recommend using a "line isolator." See Figure 3.10. This is a

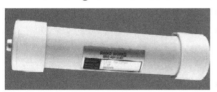

Figure 3.10
T4 Line Isolator
Courtesy of Radio Works

device that has five RF chokes inside a tube and is installed in-between the HF radio and the radio tuner--as close to the radio tuner as possible. See Appendix C under "RF Isolation" for sources of this item. It's Important to note that if your groundplane is not adequate, then all the chokes in China will not help you with your RFI problem.

HF RADIO SAFETY

Safety is another issue that needs to be addressed and taken very seriously by the HF radio user. Wherever you have your HF rig installed—be it on a boat, in your car or in your house—it is imperative that you protect others from the antenna when you are transmitting. I have seen numerous installations on sailboats where the backstay or a section of the standing rigging was used as the antenna. This is a terrific place to put an antenna. However, the backstay or standing rigging is often used as a "grab hold" to steady ones self while climbing up the swim ladder or walking around the deck of the boat.

Figures 3.11
PVC Over Backstay

By no uncertain terms should anyone be able to physically touch the section of the standing rigging that you are using for the HF antenna when you are transmitting. This includes your pets as well! If someone should touch the antenna section during an HF transmission *serious burns will result.* I have installed a section of Schedule 40 PVC pipe over my backstay for that very reason. See Figure 3.11. Schedule 40 is more resistant to the ultraviolet effects of the sun, it's inexpensive and lasts a long time. If someone needs to hold onto my backstay the PVC pipe will protect them from the antenna. Some folks place the terminal isolator and antenna feed (GTO 15) wire about seven feet up the backstay to avoid this problem. Others use the plastic sleeves that are used on sailboat standing rigging to prevent chafe on the sails. Whatever you choose to do, be safety smart. Make your antenna "Idi-Yacht" safe!

HF RADIO E-MAIL FOR "IDI-YACHTS"®
NOTES:

_____

_____

_____

_____

_____

_____

_____

_____

_____

_____

_____

_____

_____

_____

_____

_____

_____

CHAPTER 4
E-MAIL SERVICE PROVIDERS

There are two categories of service providers to choose from; an Amateur Radio (HAM) service provider or a Marine SSB commercial service provider. The differences between HAM and Marine SSB E-mail are very simple. The HAM E-mail service is free. To use HAM

radio E-mail you are required to have at least a General Class Amateur Radio license. To obtain this license you are required to pass two written exams and a 5 word per minute Morse code test. Only personal E-mails can be sent and received—no business can be conducted. Should you need to conduct business with the four letter world of work through HF radio E-mail then you must use a commercial provider.

Commercial providers charge a fee for their services. In the US, no tests are required. You must purchase two licenses from the FCC; a Ships Station License and a Restricted Radio Telephone Operator Permit. Both personal and business related E-mails can be sent and received with a commercial account. Check out Appendix D and the "Idi-Yacht" CD ROM for more information on HAM radio operator and Marine SSB licensing information.

There are several HF radio E-mail providers that offer Pactor mode E-mail. Before you can access an HF E-mail system, you must first select a service provider and register with them. Your choice of a provider will depend upon your specific communication needs and your budget. To assist you in comparing the providers, I'll list and describe key items that will have an impact on your selection.

SELECTING AN E-MAIL PROVIDER

E-MAIL SIZE LIMITATIONS

There are no size limitations from any of the HF radio E-mail providers. The size of your E-mail is limited by your batteries. Remember that HF radio E-mail is a real slow poke! Three or four half page letters sent and received per day is a reasonable expectation unless you want to be tied to the radio for a good period of time. Be sure to have your friends remove you from their joke and chain letter group mailings.

FILE ATTACHMENTS

Would you like to send some pictures to your friends, parents or grand kids to show them where you are? Check to be sure that the service provider will allow you to send and receive attachments with your E-mail. Be aware that some providers charge extra for messages with attachments. Examples of files you might want to attach to your messages include; pictures, data files, tax returns, business plans, articles and book chapters. The most economical way to send attachments would be to hold them until you get to an Internet cafe. Your batteries will thank you for that!

USER TIME LIMITS

Check to be sure that the time limits of the service provider you plan to use are in line with your projected needs

Three or four half page E-mails a day both sent and received can generally be accomplished in under ten minutes. Downloading graphic weather files or sending attachments can take a fair amount of time. This is especially true if solar flares, sunspots or atmospheric conditions are adversely affecting propagation. See the section on propagation in this Chapter and in Chapter 7 for more information on this subject.

CHAPTER 4 - HF E-MAIL SERVICE PROVIDERS
CHARGES & FEES

What is your budget for HF radio E-mail? Two commercial providers charge by the byte, or by the character. Will there be someone around to pay your bills for you while you are away? Two commercial providers charge an annual or semiannual flat fee. Be aware that there will be additional charges if you exceed a set amount of connect time with most of the flat fee providers.

COMPATIBLE HF RADIO MODEMS

All of the service providers in this guide use HF radio modems with Pactor modes. Not all providers offer Pactor-1 or even Pactor-2 operating systems. Due to the slowness of these systems, one provider who previously offered Pactor-1 and 2 modes is now using Pactor-3 mode only. This will definitely impact your selection of an HF modem. As I compare the specific service providers' features and benefits, I'll list the types of HF radio modems that are compatible with their services. Check with the service provider that you select before you purchase your modem to be sure that you have selected the appropriate equipment.

COVERAGE AREA

All of the HF radio E-mail service providers say they have worldwide coverage. Generally speaking, all of the providers should offer you accessibility during most times of the day. The key word here is accessibility. The more stations a service provider has spread across the globe, the more frequencies you will have available over a wider time and distance. This is especially important for those of you who will be going off to the "hinter land." The further away you are from a service provider's station, the fewer frequencies you will have available for a connection. See the HF Propagation section in Chapter 7 for more information.

HF RADIO E-MAIL FOR "IDI-YACHTS"®

If you want to be really sure about how easy it would be to connect to a particular service provider, download a propagation program (See the "Idi-Yacht" CD ROM). Insert the latitude and longitude of the provider's station. Then insert the latitude and longitude of the furthest distance that you plan to cruise. From this exercise, you will be able to get a general idea of which frequencies will be available at what time of the day to connect to that provider station.

WEATHER DOWNLOADS

When you're out on the "Big Blue" cruising or living in a third world country, you can't get enough weather infor-mation. Voice and text weather products, weather fax forecast charts, GOES satellite images and GRIB weather forecasts are all available for download via HF radio E-mail. Check to be sure that your provider offers these services and what the fees are (if any). If you plan on downloading GRIB weather files through the HF radio E-mail system, plan to purchase a Pactor-3 modem. You'll need all of the speed you can muster to download these files. They are loaded with data! Saildocs.com from Jim Corenman and the Sail-Mail Association can be used for these downloads. See Chapter 8 for more information.

TECHNICAL SUPPORT

There are always questions that arise, especially if you have to troubleshoot your system or the software. Knowing what technical support resources are available and how you can access them will minimize your down time and your frustration.

CHAPTER 4 - HF E-MAIL SERVICE PROVIDERS
E-MAIL ADDRESS

This address will be your HAM call sign i.e. AB1CDE@winlink.org if you use the HAM system or your ship station call sign i.e. WXY1234@theserviceprovider if you use the commercial system.

SOFTWARE

Each HF radio E-mail service provider has their own software that you must install before you can use their system. This software is available from most of the providers' WEB sites or give them a call and they'll send you a CD ROM. I've included most of the provider software programs in the "Idi-Yacht" CD ROM. Again, check to be sure you've got the most up to date version of the provider's software.

WEB PAGES UPDATED FOR CRUISERS

Some folks like to set up and maintain a cruising WEB page to let their friends and family back home have a look at where they've been. Some service providers offer a WEB page service where they will set up your page for you and add to it for a fee.

SEAMLESS INTEGRATION

Most HF E-mail providers' software also allows for accessing E-mail sent through phone Internet connections such as landlines, cellular and satellite phones. This can be a real benefit if you plan to use a satellite phone for business and HF radio E-mail for personal communications. Another advantage would be if you are away from the boat and you need to access your HF E-mail from a land line or a broadband connection. This will keep you from having to use one type of software for the HF radio E-mail and then another for your satellite phone and then another for your land line Internet connection. Another nice feature of this is that it insures that all of your E-mail addresses are located in one place. Check closely for this if you need to be able to access all of your mail and any attachments through a variety of connections. It's a great service!

PROPAGATION PROGRAMS

To successfully use HF radio E-mail you will have to make a radio connection with a service provider's station. This may

sound redundant but one thing new radio users do not realize is that not all frequencies are usable to make a connection 24 hours of the day. You will need some coaching on which frequencies to select and when to use them depending upon how far away from the service provider you are and the time of day you are trying to connect. Propagation programs that guide the user in terms of which frequencies to select based upon time of day and distance are a must.

Some service providers have an integrated propagation program within their software. Others simply provide you with suggested programs that you can use along with their HF radio E-mail software. One provider gives a propagation report but you have to connect in order to receive it.

INTERNET PAGE ACCESS

You cannot surf the net with any HF radio E-mail provider. It is possible download the text portion of a page from the Internet. To access this, you would request the page from your service provider. The service provider would go to the Internet, copy the text portion of the page and then send it to you the next time you connect to the service. Not all service providers offer this. Check closely for related fees and be advised that this could add some enormous time to your daily usage. If you must access an Internet page without fail and with all of the page graphics, then plan to use an Internet cafe or purchase a satellite phone. Saildocs.com provided by Jim Corenman is an easy way to obtain weather and Internet files. See Chapter 8 for more information.

E-MAIL COMPRESSION

All of the HF providers' software compresses E-mail files which enhances speed and efficiency especially since the HF radio E-mail system is such a slow poke. My electronic engineer mentors would like me to remind you that you can only compress water so much. Check closely regarding claims of enhanced compression services for HF E-mail to determine exactly what it is they're compressing! .

E-MAIL ENCRYPTION

The text of your messages is converted to a sort of secret code that makes it more difficult to be read by any nosey nellies. Remember that regardless of the HF radio E-mail provider you choose, there is no such thing as a completely secure digital radio connection. Information such as credit card numbers, bank account information and other confidential information is easily obtained by anyone with the proper knowledge and equipment! Be very careful when doing business over HF radio E-mail.

FREQUENCY SCANNING VS FREE SIGNAL

In frequency scanning or fixed station systems the service provider scans several frequencies with one radio. To make a connection, you have to "catch" the provider's radio when it's scanning the frequency that you are on. The provider may be occupied on another frequency—other than the one you are on. You have no way of knowing that it's busy unless you scan the other listed frequencies and hear the characteristic chirping sounds of a Pactor  transmission. Rude, ignorant operators or folks that can't hear that you are occupying the frequency can knock you off of your connection when they transmit and try to connect.

HF RADIO E-MAIL FOR "IDI-YACHTS"®

In a "free signal" system the service provider transmits a continuous free signal at all times except during a Pactor connection. There is one transmitter per frequency. If the transmitter on the frequency is idle you will hear the free signal. If you don't hear the free signal you cannot connect. Additionally, the Pactor-3 modem will connect to the service provider station only if it hears the free signal. Once you are connected and doing an active session no one can transmit and bump you off. Free signal also gives you higher availability because the transmitters are not wasting time scanning. Note that this system requires a Pactor-3 modem.

The free signal sound includes two seconds of chirping, one second of silence, and then two more seconds of chirping for fifteen seconds and then is followed by a Morse identification. Then it repeats. When I first heard this I thought that the frequency was busy! See the "Idi-Yacht" CD ROM to listen and become familiar with these sounds.

POSITION & WEATHER REPORTING

Most service providers have the ability to upload your current position onto the Internet. This is a really neat ser-

vice. Your landlubber friends and relatives can log onto the Internet and track your position. You can also find your cruising friends by requesting a position report from the provider. Another benefit of this would be in the event of a stolen boat or piracy report. The service provider can forward the report/bulletin to those in the general geographical area.

You can send measured weather reports to meteorologists who would be delighted to receive this weather data. Meteorologists welcome measured weather information if you are at sea so that they can check their models against your real-time data. Some providers have this service integrated and others do not. If your provider does not have this capability integrated into their software and you'd like to send a measured weather report when you are at sea you can send one using the YOTREPS system. See the "Idi-Yacht" CD ROM for the software.

SPAM

SPAM is the Internet's version of the telemarketer. Instead of calling you on the phone and interrupting your supper, junk mail is sent to your E-mail address. The last thing you need with the HF radio E-mail system is to have to weed through mountains of junk mail. Check to be sure your service provider has an anti-SPAM or SPAM blocking feature. One important thing you can do is to never give your HF radio E-mail address to a business on the Internet. You just never know where Spammers are lurking!

VIRUS SCANNING

The realities of the Internet will follow you even when you're out cruising the seven seas. All of the service providers scan for viruses. It would be extremely difficult to fix a virus on your computer when you're out there on the blue yonder! On your end of the line it would behoove you to have an antiviral software program that is relatively up to date and that you use regularly to download new virus definitions. Search and clean your computer of these unwanted rascals frequently! If downloading new virus definitions on a regular basis is not possible, then be advised that you may be subject to catching a new virus even with the best antiviral software! Most viruses are transmitted through attachment files. You should be very careful when you open any attached file. Be sure you know the source of the attachment. If you don't know the source, then delete it immediately!

HAM E-MAIL PROVIDERS

Winlink 2000 (WL2K) is the one and only HAM HF radio E-mail provider. The stations that comprise this system are referred to as PMBO's; Participating Mail Box Offices. For more information, check out their WEB site: http://www.winlink.org. Steve Waterman, K4CJX, is the system administrator and can be reached by E-mail at: K4CJX@comcast.net or at K4CJX@winlink.org. There are important items that are specific to using this system. Below I will directly quote the information from the Winlink 2000 WEB site regarding business use, and third party traffic rules. Use of this system requires you to read, to understand and to follow these rules!

PERSONAL OR BUSINESS USE DEFINED

"Directly or indirectly enhancing one's pecuniary interest over amateur radio is universally prohibited. Such traffic is any message that is related to an amateur's business or other activity involved in *making* money or attempting to make money for the amateur. Such things as placing orders to trade stocks are a clear-cut example of disallowed message content. On the other hand, in the US, the FCC has opinioned that merely ordering items for personal use is not in violation of the rules so long as it is incidental to your activity as an amateur and not to enhance your pecuniary interest."

THIRD PARTY TRAFFIC

"Third-party traffic is any traffic transmitted over the Amateur bands that is either from or to a non-amateur. In the Western Hemisphere (with a few exceptions) there is no restriction on third-party traffic being passed over amateur radio. Many countries outside of the Western Hemisphere also now permit third-party traffic over amateur radio. Messages between amateurs even if they originate or are delivered over Internet are not considered third-party traffic. Third-party traffic only deals with that portion which is transmitted over the radio spectrum."

"Since there is no limitation on third-party traffic over Internet itself, messages passed between WL2K participating stations, or a participating station and the Internet are *not* restricted. Only when the message involves a non-amateur and is passed over a radio link is the issue a concern. For example: if a message originates in the U.K. on Internet but is delivered to a US. Amateur over the radio from a US-based station no third-party rule is broken even though the U.K. does not allow third-party traffic over amateur channels. Likewise, a message originating over the radio from a US Amateur and passed to a US station is legal even if it is addressed to the Internet address of a non-amateur in the U.K."

"Users must make themselves familiar with these third-party rules for the country in which they are operating as well as linking with if they are exchanging messages with non-amateurs." See the Winlink WEB site or the ARRL WEB site at http://www.arrl.org for countries known to permit third-party traffic for US stations and their reciprocals.

E-MAIL SIZE LIMITATIONS

None. There are recommendations depending upon which Pactor mode you use that will help you avoid spending a lot of time and battery power sending and receiving your E-mail. See "File Attachments" below. You can also defer or reject incoming E-mail based upon the size of the message. See the AirMail help files to set up this option in the software.

FILE ATTACHMENTS

The size of your file attachments (and total outgoing file size) with the WL2K system are limited by your batteries! Steve Waterman recommends the following for total file size: Pactor-1 a maximum file size of 10,000 bytes, Pactor-2 a maximum of 50,000 bytes and Pactor-3 a maximum of 80,000 bytes. For those of you using the Pactor-3 protocol remember that depending upon atmospheric conditions, your speed could drop to the Pactor-2 level and slow to 200 bits per second!

HF RADIO E-MAIL FOR "IDI-YACHTS"®

Attachments to messages must be file types with extensions that can be viewed with commonly available software such as .doc, .rtf, .jpg, .bmp, etc. WL2K will not accept executable files from Internet with extensions such as .exe, .com, .vbs, etc. This reduces the chance of passing a file containing a virus.

USER TIME LIMITS

Generally 30 minutes a day. Each PMBO sets their own time limit. Limits can be increased by sending a request to the individual PMBO; i.e.: KN6KB@winlink.org.

CHARGES & FEES

The service is free to licensed General, Advanced and Amateur Extra class Amateur radio operators (HAMS). Check out Appendix D for information on how to become a licensed HAM radio operator.

COMPATIBLE HF RADIO MODEMS

The Winlink system uses Pactor technology exclusively. AirMail supports the SCS PTC-II Pro and PTC-IIe, PTC-IIex, and PTC-II Pactor-2 modems as well as the original PTC Pactor-1 modem, the Kantronics KAM+ and KAM-98, AEA/Timewave PK-232, PK-900, DSP-1232 and 2232, the MFJ 1276 and 1278B, and the HAL DXP-38 Clover/Pactor modem. (Sound cards are not supported).

Some of the Winlink PMBO stations are now moving away from Pactor-1 as it is too slow and is clogging up the system. These are designated as "Express Stations" in the Coverage Area section below. Be sure to make a note of this when you are pricing and making your decision regarding which modem to purchase. With technology changing so rapidly, I'd recommend that you purchase an HF modem capable of Pactor-2 mode that can be later upgraded to Pactor-3. Who knows when Pactor-4 will be available!

COVERAGE AREA

Participating stations (PMBOs) are available worldwide. Below is a current list of Winlink stations as of this writing:

Austria -	OE4XBU -	Rudy in Eisenstadt *
Australia -	VK8HF -	John in Darwin
	VK6KPS -	Phil in Perth*
Canada -	VE6KBS -	Karl in Calgary, Alberta *
	VE2AFQ -	Andre in Montreal *
Caribbean -	WG3G -	Bernie in Trinidad
	ZF1GC -	Frank in Grand Cayman Is *
	NP2E -	Bernie, St. Thomas, VI *
Germany -	DA5UAW -	Andi in Rudolstadt
Italy -	IV3XHR -	Gianpaolo in Udine *
Middle East -	A71BY -	Jabor & Murali, in Qatar*
Netherlands-	PA3DUV -	Dick in the Netherlands *
New Zealand-	ZL1MA -	Arnold in Auckland
	ZL2UT -	Basil in Gisborne
South Africa-	ZS5S -	Joost in Howick
Sweden -	SM6USU -	Svante Glose
Thailand -	HS0AC -	Rudolph in Bangkok *
United States & Hawaii -		
	AB7AA -	Bill in Oahu, Hawaii *
	AH6QK -	Richard in Oahu, Hawaii *
	K4CJX -	Steve in Nashville, TN *+
	K4SET -	Scott in Murray, Kentucky *
	K6IXA -	Grady in Atwater, CA *
	K6CYC -	Scott in Los Angeles, CA *
	K7AAE -	Ronald in Washington *
	KA6IQA -	Tom in California *
	KA7CTT -	Lynn in Vancouver, Washington
	KB6YNO -	Eric South Portland, Maine *
	KN6KB -	Rick in Rockledge, Florida *
	N8PGR -	Hans in North Royalton, Ohio *
	N0IA -	Bud in Deltona, Florida *
	W1ON -	Doc in Bedford, Mass.*
	W6IM -	Rod in San Diego, CA *
	W7BO -	John in Woodland, Washington*
	W9MR -	Kenn in keensburg, Illinois
	W9GSS -	Charles in East Peoria, Illinois *

WA2DXQ -   Dave in Ft. Lauderdale, Florida *
WB0TAX -   Deni in Elm Grove, Louisiana *+
WB5KSD -   Jon in Farmersville, Texas
WD8DHF -   Gary in Harker Heights, Texas *

The * denotes a "Fastlink" station. A Fastlink station is continuously connected to the Internet. When you send them your E-mail it is uploaded almost instantly to the Internet. Non Fastlink stations will log onto the Internet at periodic times of the day and send/receive your E-mail. The + indicate "Express" stations that offer Pactor-2 and 3 connections only.

WEATHER DOWNLOADS

Winlink (WL2K) uses an "on-demand" bulletin distribution mechanism. Users must first select requested bulletins from an available "catalog" managed in AirMail. When bulletin requests are received by a PMBO, a copy of the requested bulletin is sent and usually received at the next log in. The catalog currently includes over 700 available weather, propagation, and information bulletins. All WL2K PMBOs support a single Global catalog which insures users can access *any* bulletin from *any* PMBO. Bulletins can contain basic text, graphic fax or satellite images, binary or encoded files like GRIB or WMO weather reports.

You can also use the Winlink system to receive text or GRIB weather forecasts by way of the AirMail catalog/bulletin files. More information on what GRIB files are and how you can receive them will be discussed in Chapter 8. Be sure to note that if you intend to download GRIB weather files that you should plan on buying a Pactor-3 modem. The files are large and the downloads can take a while.

TECHNICAL SUPPORT

WL2K is supported by its participating stations (PM-BOs), the many vendors who supply equipment, the author of AirMail and the Winlink development team. The point of contact for assistance with this system is the system administrator, Steve Waterman, K4CJX. Depending upon the particular questions or issues, Steve will seek the assistance of others for you as required. Support contact should be made to Steve at: K4CJX@comcast.net or K4CJX@winlink.org.

In addition, for those within reach, an "AirMail Technical Support Net" is held every Thursday after the Waterway Radio and Cruising Club Net ends which is around 8:30 Eastern Time (ET) on 7.268, LSB. This is a HAM frequency and you must have at least a General class license to transmit and join in. The AirMail Primer, located for downloading from their WEB site is chock full of valuable information and resources. The AirMail help file, located within the software program, is also full of useful information.

E-MAIL ADDRESS

YourHAMcallsign@winlink.org

SOFTWARE

AirMail is the software program that you will use if you plan on accessing the Winlink HAM HF E-mail system. The software is free and available on the Internet for downloading at: http://www.airmail2000.com and in the "Idi-Yacht" CD ROM. The "Winlink 2000" CD ROM is available for a nominal charge of $15 (US). The CD ROM is available from K4CJX@winlink.org or KN6KB@winlink.org or you can buy it at the Seven Seas Cruising Association's GAM which is held each November in Melbourne, Florida.

The software is updated at least once yearly. Before you go off on your cruise, be sure to check and see that you have the latest version, with the latest list of PMBOs, their frequencies and the Winlink catalog/bulletins. Don't leave port without first checking their WEB site. The version included with this book in the "Idi-Yacht" CD ROM is 3.1.921.

WEB PAGES UPDATED FOR CRUISERS

A cruising WEB site update service is not offered. However, users of this system can update their WEB pages. See the following site for more information:
http://www.winlink.org/links.htm

SEAMLESS INTEGRATION

You can access your HF E-Mail through a land line Internet connection in two ways; using the WEB Browser access or the TelNet option. This WEB Browser Access is limited to text-based messages only. Bulletins, GRIB weather files or file attachments are not accessible by this method. E-mail addresses can be imported to AirMail from most E-mail programs. You can also forward your HF E-mail to an ISP provider such as Yahoo, Netzero, etc. See the AirMail Help file or Chapter 6 for how to set this up. TelNet is a new service that you can use to access your HF radio E-mail and attachments through the Internet. See the AirMail "Help Files" for more information on how to set this up.

Winlink 2000 TELPAC

This is a new product for delivering mail from the Winlink 2000 system to a wireless ham user. *"TELPAC"* stands for TELnet PACket Bridge. *TELPAC* is optimized to easily interface Winlink 2000 to conventional VHF/UHF Packet users and BBSs. This includes simple portable terminals (e.g. Palm devices) as well as more capable FBB compatible programs including *AirMail* packet. Check out the enclosed "Idi-Yacht" CD ROM or the Winlink WEB site for more information: http://www.winlink.org.

PROPAGATION PROGRAMS

The "ITSHF" propagation program has been integrated into the AirMail software program and is available for downloading on their WEB site. See also the "Using HAM radio E-mail" section in chapter 7 or the AirMail help file for more information. The "Idi-Yacht" CD ROM includes a copy of the software.

INTERNET PAGE ACCESS

There are over 700 WEB pages that are listed, maintained and available for download in the AirMail catalog section. Topics of these pages include news, weather forecasts and piracy reports. Additional WEB pages are available upon request.

E-MAIL COMPRESSION

Automatically provided.

E-MAIL ENCRYPTION

Data transmissions of E-mail to and from the Winlink stations can be sent in what's called a binary format. If someone can read your data transmissions, all they will see is a bunch of computer characters. Professional spies will be able to read your mail but nosey nellies will not. Check out the AirMail help file for more information on how to set this up.

FREQUENCY SCANNING VS FREE SIGNAL

This provider stations use frequency scanning or fixed station frequencies.

POSITION & WEATHER REPORTING

Winlink provides rapid position reporting from anywhere in the World. You must configure this option and enter your current position in the AirMail software for this to work. This is done either manually or by interfacing a GPS. When you make a connection to a PMBO, your position is automatically uploaded onto the Internet. Your landlubber friends can find you by entering your call sign in the Winlink APRS WEB site which is located at: http://www.winlink.org/aprs.

HF RADIO E-MAIL FOR "IDI-YACHTS"®

Winlink also supports weather reporting from cruising yachts at sea with an interconnection with the NWS/NOAA MAROB weather entry system. This is used by US government forecasters for weather observations at sea where no others are available. Check out the AirMail "Help Files" and Chapter 8 for more details.

SPAM

WL2K subscribes to several professional services including "SPAM COP" that catch most of the E-mail SPAM that originates from the Internet. However, there is no such thing as a SPAM proof service.

Jim Corenman, the author of AirMail recommends the following steps to help avoid SPAM. If you have a web site, or contribute to a web site, never post your E-mail address to the WEB site (or allow someone else to be post it). Never send anything to an Internet newsgroup or WEB based "forum" of any sort which includes your radio E-mail address. Avoid using your radio E-mail address when filling out an on-line form or ordering anything on-line. Get a free Hotmail or Yahoo E-mail address and use that instead. Periodically do an Internet search for your radio E-mail address(es), using search engines such as Google at: http://www.google.com or Metcrawler located at: http://www.metcrawler.com. If you find your address posted somewhere, get if off. There is no assurance that you will find it before the Spammers.

VIRUS SCANNING

All Winlink stations scan for viruses. Although there has never been a virus passed through the WL2K system, they recommend that you have an antiviral program installed on your hard drive and that you update it regularly.

COMMERCIAL E-MAIL PROVIDERS

There are two types of commercial providers; private and public. The private provider has a requirement that  vessels be under 1600 tons. Users of this system will need to keep copies of all of the private provider's coast station licenses on board their vessel. To date, the SailMail Association is the only private coast station. There are no such restrictions or requirements with the public providers. Before you can set up an account with any of the service providers you will need the appropriate licenses. If you haven't applied for your licenses I would suggest doing so as soon as possible. You will be dealing with a government entity to obtain these licenses. The time involved in processing your application will vary. In the US you can file over the Internet and receive your license in about a day or so. See Appendix D and the "Idi-Yacht" CD ROM for more information on Marine SSB licensing.

Please note that the author has no financial affiliation whatsoever with any of these providers. They are listed in alphabetical order for reader convenience. The information on the service providers has been obtained from their WEB sites and where possible, directly from them. It is highly recommended that you carefully read and compare the providers' products. Be sure to inquire about any changes in services and fees that may have occurred since this publication was printed. See Appendix B for service provider contact information.

This section will outline the features and benefits of four HF radio E-mail commercial providers. There are many similarities to each of the service providers and some very interesting differences. On the following page is a quick reference guide that summarizes the features and benefits for each of the providers.

Commercial HF E-mail Provider Chart

SP	MarineNet	SailMail	SeaWave	ShipCom
TYPE	P	NP	P	P
ESIZE	N	N	N	N
ATTCH	Y	NA*	Y	Y
AFEE	N	N	Y	Y
TLIMIT	600/M	AVG 300/M	N	N
FEES	A	A	B	B
MODE	3	1,2,3	3	1,2,3
COVRG	4	13	6	1
WX	Y	Y	Y	Y
FWX	N	N	Y	Y
CWPU	Y	N	N	N
SI	Y	Y	Y	Y
IPROP	N	Y	N	N
IPA	Y	Y	Y	Y
FIPA	N	N	Y	Y
COMPR	Y	Y	Y	Y
ENCRP	Y	N	N	N
POSRPT	Y	Y	Y	Y
WXRPT	Y	Y	N	Y
SPAM	Y	Y	Y	Y

SP:	*Service Provider*	*NA= Not Applicable*	*Y=Yes N=No*
TYPE:	*P= Public Coast Station*	*NP= Private Coast Station*	
ESIZE:	*E-mail size limitations*	*N=None*	
ATTCH:	*File attachments Allowed*	*NA*= GRIB Wx files only*	
AFEE:	*File attachment fees*		
TLIMIT:	*Connect time limit; minutes per (M) Month*		
FEES:	*A= Flat Fee*	*B= Charge Per Kilobyte*	
MODE:	*1= Pactor-1*	*2= Pactor-2*	*3= Pactor-3*
COVRG:	*Number of stations*		
WXD:	*Weather Downloads*		
FWX:	*Fees charged for weather downloads*		
CWPU:	*Cruising Web Page Update services*		
SI:	*Seamless Integration*		
IPROP:	*Integrated Propagation Program*		
IPA:	*Internet Page Access*		
FIPA:	*Fees for accessing an Internet Page*		
COMPR:	*Compression Services Available*		
ENCRP:	*Encryption Services*		
POSRPT:	*Position Reporting*		
WXRPT:	*Weather Reporting*		
SPAM:	*Junk Mail Filtering capability*		

MarineNet Wireless

John Heron
17940 Loxahatchee River Road, Jupiter, Florida 33458
Phone:561-747-5686 Fax:561-747-9357
E-mail: service@marinenet.net
WEB: http://www.marinenet.net

E-MAIL SIZE LIMITATIONS

No limit to the size of the E-mail except for your batteries!

FILE ATTACHMENTS

Full support for file attachments and no additional charges for attachments.

USER TIME LIMITS

600 minutes a month (10 hours). If more time is needed it can be purchased. Check with the service provider for current pricing.

CHARGES & FEES

MarineNet Wireless offers 600 minutes of Pactor-3 usage per month for $23 a month (paid bi-yearly, or yearly). Users can purchase additional time if their usage needs are greater than 600 minutes a month.

COMPATIBLE HF RADIO MODEMS

Pactor-3 mode only. SCS PTC-II, SCS PTC-IIe, SCS PTC-IIex or SCS PTC-Pro with upgrade to Pactor-3 operating protocol. Company can provide Pactor-3 upgrade or Pactor-3 ready modems.

COVERAGE AREA

WKS - Indiantown, FL   **DZO** - Manila, Italy
WLC - Rogers City, Michigan   **DAO** - Kiel, Germany

HF RADIO E-MAIL FOR "IDI-YACHTS"®
WEATHER DOWNLOADS

Available at no charge. There is no internal drop down menu in the software that you can point to and click on to request weather downloads. Contact the service provider for more information.

TECHNICAL SUPPORT

M-F 0900-1700 EDT. Phone: 561-747-5686 Fax: 561-747-9357. E-mail:service@marinenet.net. MarineNet Wireless requests that you contact them through E-mail. That way your technical question can be answered promptly.

E-MAIL ADDRESS

Station call sign (WXY1234)@marinenet.net

SOFTWARE

Uses proprietary Calypso software. You can obtain the software from the provider or you can download it from their Internet site: http://www.marinenet.net, or from the "Idi-Yacht" CD ROM.

WEB PAGES UPDATED FOR CRUISERS

This service is offered and provides for an indirect update where files are sent to a special E-mail address. The service provider then updates your cruising web page with the information you send them. Extra charges apply. Check with the service provider for current fees and procedures.

SEAMLESS INTEGRATION

The user does not need to change E-mail programs when he or she is off the boat. HF radio E-mail can be accessed using a land line Internet connection. Check their WEB site for more information.

PROPAGATION PROGRAMS

None. The provider uses "Free Signal" tones where you can check propagation by listening for these sounds. If you hear them clearly, then you should have good propagation. If they are weak then you need to select another frequency. See the "Idi-Yacht" CD ROM for examples of these sounds.

E-MAIL COMPRESSION

Automatically provided.

INTERNET PAGE ACCESS

Available. Contact the provider for details.

E-MAIL ENCRYPTION

Uses a simple binary type of data transmission that makes it impossible for typical users to read your mail. If you need a comprehensive encryption system they offer the PGP or "Pretty Good Protection" system for encrypting E-mail for no charge. Both you and the parties that you will be E-mailing will need to have PGP installed in order to read the E-mails sent and received using this software. Note that professional spies can still decode your messages!

FREQUENCY SCANNING VS FREE SIGNAL

The provider is in the process of converting all stations to the "Free Signal" mode as of September 2003.

POSITION & WEATHER REPORTING

YOTREPS position & weather reporting are available.

SPAM

Anti-SPAM products used at the provider server. If a problem with SPAM develops, contact the service provider for technical support. The best way to avoid SPAM is to prevent it by not listing your HF radio E-mail address on WEB pages or giving it out when ordering items on the Internet.

VIRUS SCANNING

MarineNet Wireless provides server side virus scanning which scans every E-mail and attachment sent or received for viruses. They also recommend that you only open attached files from users known to you. If you plan to install an antiviral software program, they strongly recommend that you get the updates on a regular basis. Don't be fooled into thinking you are protected unless you routinely download the new virus definitions!

SailMail

SailMail Association, Jim Corenman & Stan Honey
921 E. Charleston Road, Palo Alto, CA, 94303, USA
Phone: 619-980-6215
E-Mail: sysop@sailmail.com
WEB: http://www.sailmail.com

The SailMail Association has the most stations and the widest global coverage of any provider. SailMail Association members must download, print and keep a copy of the stations on board their vessel. See the SailMail WEB site for more information.

E-MAIL SIZE LIMITATIONS

Unlimited outgoing. Limited only by your batteries!

FILE ATTACHMENTS

Only GRIB weather files. See the SailMail WEB site or the "Help Files" for more information. GRIB file access uses the excellent and free of charge saildocs.com service provided by Jim Corenman.

USER TIME LIMITS

Very flexible. Members are requested to limit time on the system to an average of about 10 minutes per day.

CHARGES & FEES

Two hundred dollars (US) for one year. All users of the SailMail service must join the SailMail Association in order to access the stations. The membership fee is $200 per vessel, per year. This is subject to change in the future as the number of members, the cost of station operation, and the cost of setting up additional stations vary. Application processing time is approximately one week.

COMPATIBLE HF RADIO MODEMS

Pactor 1, 2 and 3 operating modes. SailMail supports all Pactor mode HF modems with the exception of the SG-7200.

HF RADIO E-MAIL FOR "IDI-YACHTS"®
COVERAGE AREA

Worldwide. Below is a list of participating stations:

Australia -	VZX -	Firefly, NSW, Australia
Belgium -	OSY -	Brugge, Belgium
Nova Scotia -	XJN7 -	Lunenburg, NS
Panama -	HPPM2 -	Pedro Miguel, Panama
Southern Africa -	RC01 -	Maputo, Mozambique
Southeast Asia -	V8V2222 -	Brunei Darussalam
United States -	WRD719 -	Palo Alto, California
	WHV861 -	San Luis, California
	WHV3822 -	Friday Harbor,WA
	KUZ533 -	Honolulu, Hawaii
	KZN508 -	Rockhill, S. Carolina
	WPTG385 -	Corpus Christi, Texas
	WPUC469 -	South Daytona, Florida

WEATHER DOWNLOADS

You can receive text or GRIB weather forecasts at no charge. The easiest way is to use saildocs.com, a free service of Jim Corenman. For information on how to request weather files, send an E-mail to info@saildocs.com or see Chapter 8 for more information.

You can use SailMail to communicate with a meteorologist or commercial weather service, who can advise you on good departure dates and routes, and can send you custom GRIB files for a fee. See the FAQ section of the SailMail Primer for a list of meteorologists and commercial weather services who are expert at advising cruisers.

TECHNICAL SUPPORT

Technical support is available by phone or E-mail. The hours for phone support are 8AM-6PM Pacific Time Mon-Fri and 10AM-5PM Pacific Time Sat-Sun. The SailMail Primer and the help files are extensive and informative. The E-mail address for technical support is sysop@sailmail.com.

CHAPTER 4 - HF E-MAIL SERVICE PROVIDERS
E-MAIL ADDRESS

Your ship station call sign (WXY1234)@sailmail.com.

POSITION & WEATHER REPORTING

SailMail supports the YOTREPS position reporting system. Consult the SailMail Help files for details. SailMail supports weather reporting from cruising yachts at sea with an interconnection with the NOAA MAROB weather entry system. This is used by US government forecasters for weather observations at sea where no others are available.

SOFTWARE

AirMail is the software program that you will use if you plan on accessing the SailMail Association's system. The software is free and available from the SailMail Association, on their Internet site at:http://www.sailmail.com and in the enclosed "Idi-Yacht" CD ROM. The software is updated at least once yearly. Before you go off on your cruise, be sure to check and see that you have the latest version, with the latest list of PMBOs, their frequencies and the Winlink catalog/bulletins. The version included with this book in the "Idi-Yacht" CD ROM is 3.1.921.

WEB PAGES UPDATED FOR CRUISERS

This service is not available.

SEAMLESS INTEGRATION

You can access your SailMail messages through an Internet connection. See the SailMail "Help Files" or their WEB site on "WEB Mail" for more information on how to set this up.

PROPAGATION PROGRAMS

Integrated using the freeware program "ITSHF." It is very easy to use within the AirMail/SailMail software!

INTERNET PAGE ACCESS

Available through saildocs.com. Any WEB page can be retrieved (except redirected pages) and converted to plain text format. Send an E-mail to info@saildocs.com.

HF RADIO E-MAIL FOR "IDI-YACHTS"®

E-MAIL COMPRESSION

Automatically provided by the AirMail software program.

E-MAIL ENCRYPTION

Uses a binary format that can't be read by the nosey nellies.

FREQUENCY SCANNING VS FREE SIGNAL

The SailMail stations use frequency scanning.

SPAM

The best approach to SPAM is to prevent it from happening in the first place. NEVER, EVER post your radio E-mail address on a WEB site. NEVER use your radio E-mail address on an on-line form. And do NOT allow your friends to include your address with a hundred others on their joke lists or "virus alert" messages. If you must give an E-mail address on a form, maintain another E-mail account such as a Yahoo or a Netzero account. See the following sites: http://www.yahoo.com or http://www.netzero.com or http://www.popmail.com for more information on these free accounts. Always use one of these freebie addresses if you have to put an E-mail address on any form, particularly on the WEB. If you develop a problem with SPAM, contact the SailMail Association for assistance.

VIRUS SCANNING

The SailMail Internet Gateway system scans all messages for viruses, and since email attachments are not forwarded there is no possibility of receiving a virus via your Sailmail address. If you take your computer ashore, the SailMail Association recommends buying and installing an antiviral software program and keeping it and your virus definitions up to date!

SeaWave, LLC

76 Hammarlund Way Middletown, RI 02842
Phone: 401-846-8403, 800-746-6251 Fax: 401-846-9012
E-mail: info@seawave.com WEB: http://www.seawave.com

This company specializes in installations typically aboard commercial vessels with large crew. Cruising vessels of any size are welcome.

E-MAIL SIZE LIMITATIONS

None. In large commercial vessel installations with multiple users, the size of an E-mail both inbound and outbound can be limited by the vessel's system administrator.

FILE ATTACHMENTS

Available. No size limitations other than as above. If you receive a large file attachment at sea you can leave the message on the system and download it for free from a land based Internet connection. The vessel's system administrator can limit the size of file attachments both inbound and outbound.

USER TIME LIMITS

Since you are charged by the character there is no daily or monthly limit on E-mail usage.

CHARGES & FEES

Charges are by the byte. Contact sales@seawave.com for current pricing.

COMPATIBLE HF RADIO MODEMS

Uses proprietary hardware called the SeaWave Navigator 2.0. The unit comes bundled with a DSP modem and all necessary cables. The HF modem is not compatible for use with other HF E-mail providers.

HF RADIO E-MAIL FOR "IDI-YACHTS"®
COVERAGE AREA

Stations are located in Alaska, Rhode Island, Texas, Washington, Switzerland and Germany.

WEATHER DOWNLOADS

Additional fees apply; 1.95^1 for full color and 0.95^1 for text weather and buoy forecasts. Users can download a wide variety of weather products directly through the system and/or use MaxSeaWeather to access these products.

TECHNICAL SUPPORT

By phone or E-mail 24 hours a day, 7 days a week. Comprehensive on-line knowledge base available at: http://my.seawave.net.

E-MAIL ADDRESS

Supports multiple users on one account and provides for the use of vanity call signs, i.e. mbrown@seawave.net.

POSITION & WEATHER REPORTING

Free tracking tool for the vessel's position based on GPS coordinates. Weather is often reported by their customers using the commercial vessel Voluntary Observing Ship program (VOS), a program of the NWS.

SOFTWARE

Uses proprietary software SeaWave Navigator 2.0.

WEB PAGES UPDATED FOR CRUISERS

Not Available.

SEAMLESS INTEGRATION

Users can also access their HF radio E-mail messages from a land based Internet connection. Large files can be saved and downloaded later from an Internet connection.

---

1 - Prices are as of September 2003, in US dollars.

PROPAGATION PROGRAMS

None needed. The system continuously scans all available HF frequencies. When an HF radio E-mail or a communication task is initiated, the system automatically tunes the radio for the best frequency to route the E-mail.

INTERNET PAGE ACCESS

Internet pages and all weather products are available for download as well as news. There are fees for this service.

E-MAIL COMPRESSION

Uses proprietary SeaWave Throughput Technology Software (TTS) that breaks down each message, both incoming and outgoing, into multiple parts that are individually compressed for greater speed and efficiency.

E-MAIL ENCRYPTION

Available with the Integrator 3.0 only.

FREQUENCY SCANNING VS FREE SIGNAL

The provider uses free signal technology. Selection of a clear frequency is automatically performed by the software system when an E-mail or communication request is initiated by the user. These features are part of their patent pending ALE technology that brings completely automated operation to the HF radio.

SPAM

Uses a junk mail filtering system that can be configured by the individual user.

VIRUS SCANNING

All files and attachments are scanned for viruses.

ShipCom, LLC

Rene Stiegler
7700 Rinla Avenue Mobile, Alabama 36619
Phone: 251-666-5110
E-mail: info@wloradio.com
WEB: http://www.wloradio.com http://www.shipcom.com

E-MAIL SIZE LIMITATIONS

No limitations except for your batteries. See below for guidelines.

FILE ATTACHMENTS

Available. Recommended total file size including attachments should be 10K for Pactor-1, 50K for Pactor-2, and 80K for Pactor-3.

USER TIME LIMITS

Since you are charged by the character there is no daily or monthly limit on E-mail usage.

CHARGES & FEES

Give them a call for their current promotional specials.

COMPATIBLE HF RADIO MODEMS

Any Pactor-1, 2, or 3 capable modem.

COVERAGE AREA

WLO station located in Mobile, Alabama, overlooking the Gulf of Mexico with an enormous array of antennas.

WEATHER DOWNLOADS

Available free of charge when user providers weather reports using VOS and AMVERS.

TECHNICAL SUPPORT

24 hours a day and 7 days a week.

E-MAIL ADDRESS

Yourshipcallsign@wloradio.com

POSITION & WEATHER REPORTING

Position reports available through ShipTrak. Weather reporting is welcomed.

SOFTWARE

Uses any "Dumb" terminal software program. A new Windows based client software program will be released in the near future.

WEB PAGES UPDATED FOR CRUISERS

No formal service.

SEAMLESS INTEGRATION

Users can access their HF E-mail through an Internet connection.

PROPAGATION PROGRAMS

None integrated. Top of the hour broadcasts with abbreviated weather reports and vessel traffic lists can be used as a check of propagation.

INTERNET PAGE ACCESS

Available upon request.

E-MAIL COMPRESSION

Standard Pactor protocol compression.

E-MAIL ENCRYPTION

Standard binary mode.

FREQUENCY SCANNING VS FREE SIGNAL

The provider uses dedicated radios for each listed frequency.

SPAM

Uses a junk mail filtering system. Don't forget that an ounce of prevention is worth a pound of cure. Don't post your radio E-mail on the WEB for any reason!

HF RADIO E-MAIL FOR "IDI-YACHTS"®
VIRUS SCANNING

All files and attachments are scanned for viruses.

MARINE SSB & VHF PHONE SERVICES

ShipCom's WLO[1] station delivers messages to and from vessels via E-mail, Satellite, SITOR, RTTY, Fax, SSB and VHF. They also offer News, Weather, Media Content, and more thru the WLO Radio network. Their newest station, KLB[1] in Seattle, is now operational for Marine SSB phone services. Radio Operators are on duty 24/7 for your communication needs.

Below are their fees for phone calls with the "Premium Account."
WLO HF-Voice Telephone Premium Account[1,2]
$2.99/min Calls TO USA & Canada
$3.99/min Call TO OUTSIDE USA & Canada

On the 4 MHz frequencies all calls TO USA & Canada are $0.99/min.

Customers must register with their credit card information to start a Premium Account. You can register by sending an E-mail with your credit card, name and ship station license information to wloradio@wloradio.com. Collect calls and third party billing is now available.

---

1 - See the "Idi-Yacht" CD ROM for Marine SSB station frequencies.
2 - Prices are as of September 2003, in US dollars.

Below are the fees for phone calls with a "Standard Account."

WLO HF-Voice Telephone Standard Rates[1,2]
High Seas Ship - Shore Calls TO USA & Canada:
$3.99 per minute 3 minute minimum
Calls TO OUTSIDE of USA & Canada:
$4.99 per minute 3 minute minimum.

Below are the fees for the Marine VHF phone services:

VHF/CH(MF)-Voice Telephone[2]
From Texas to the tip of Florida
$0.99/min for calls TO USA & Canada
$1.99/min for calls TO OUTSIDE USA & Canada

---

1 - See the "Idi-Yacht" CD ROM for Marine SSB station frequencies.
2 - Prices are as of September 2003, in US dollars.

HF RADIO E-MAIL FOR "IDI-YACHTS"®
NOTES:

_____

_____

_____

_____

_____

_____

_____

_____

_____

_____

_____

_____

_____

_____

_____

CHAPTER 5
EQUIPMENT CONNECTIONS

Now that you have fined tuned the installation of your HF radio, selected your HF modem and your service provider, the next step will be to connect all of the pieces. This can be one of the most confusing steps in the HF Radio E-mail system setup. Three separate

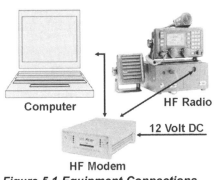

connections must be made to the HF modem. The modem must be connected to the computer, to the HF radio and to a 12 volt battery source. See Figure 5.1. This chapter will provide you with instructions on how to make these connections.

Figure 5.1 Equipment Connections
M-802 Courtesy of Icom America
PTC II-ex Courtesy of SCS GmbH & Co.

MODEM TO COMPUTER CONNECTIONS

The HF modem must be connected to your computer so that the computer and the modem can talk to each other. See Figure 5.2. A shielded 9 pin RS232 computer cable is used for this connection. They are about six feet long so plan your installation accordingly. These cables are ready made and available at any computer, office supply or electronics supply store.

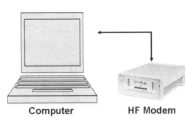

Figure 5.2
Computer To Modem Connection
PTC-IIex Courtesy of SCS GmbH & Co.

There are two ends on a RS232 cable and several variations of the sizes of the ends. You will need one end

to be a female nine pin connector. This female nine pin connector connects to the male nine pin serial port in the back of your computer. The second end of the RS232 cable that connects

Figure 5.3
9 Pin RS232 Plugs

to the back of your HF modem will be a 9 pin male. See Figure 5.3 for examples of the male and female nine pin RS232 cable plugs.

USB To Serial Port Converters

Most new laptop computers are now coming equipped with only USB ports. If you computer does not have a nine

pin male RS232 serial port, then you will have to purchase a USB to Serial Port Converter like the one in Figure 5.4. I've listed sources in Appendix C of these converters that are tried and true.

Install the software for the converter as instructed. Connect the USB end of the converter to a USB port on the back of your computer. Take the six foot RS232 cable and connect the male end to the female end of the USB converter. The

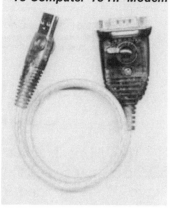

To Computer To HF Modem

Figure 5.4
USB to Serial Port Converter
Courtesy of Buck Rodgers, K4ABT

length of the converter cable is usually too short to reach from the modem to the back of your computer so you will use the RS232 cable as an extension chord. Last but not least you will connect the remaining nine pin RS232 male plug to the back of your HF modem. You're in business!

MODEM POWER CONNECTIONS

You must connect the modem to a DC or 12 volt battery power source that uses a negative ground. You have two options for this connection. You can connect it to the DIN plug in the radio or directly from the modem to the power source. If the length from the TNC to the radio is greater than four feet I'd recommend you use a separate power connection.

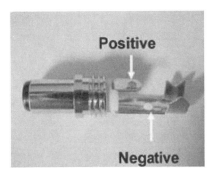

Figure 5.5
Modem Power Plug Wiring

Don't forget to put an in-line fuse on the battery positive side. A one amp fuse ought to be sufficient--most modems draw less than 0.5 amps. Consult your modem manual for the specifics on your modem. Check your radio manual to determine if you can wire the power directly through the DIN plug from the radio. Also of note. All of the SCS modems have the center of the power plug as battery positive. See Figure 5.5. If you are using another brand of modem, check your technical specifications for information on how to make these connections.

MODEM TO RADIO CONNECTIONS

The HF modem must be connected to the radio so that they can communicate with each other. This connection is accomplished using a shielded 8 strand wire that has a DIN plug on both ends. See Figure 5.6 on the following page. Most modem manufacturers will provide you with a cable that has one plug already configured for the modem. The DIN plug that connects to the radio will depend upon which type of radio you have. Unfortunately, there is no universal standard amongst the various brands of HF radios for DIN connec-tions to HF modems.

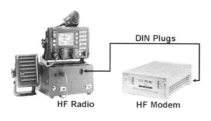

Figure 5.6
HF Radio To Modem Connections
M-802 Courtesy of Icom America,
PTC II-ex Courtesy of SCS GmbH & Co.

When I got my first modem and opened the box, the cable in Figure 5.7 was what I had to work with. At the time I had no earthly idea of what to do with it!

You have two options for configuring your radio connection; you can purchase a pre-made cable or you can make your own. If you're truly soldering impaired, go ahead and buy a ready made cable. I don't recommend this especially if your installation is on a boat and you plan to go off cruising. It's best to learn how to make the plug before you leave just in case you need to fix it while you're off in the islands. See the "HF Modem to Radio DIN Cables," "Marine SSB Radio Systems

Figure 5.7 DIN Plug & Wire
Courtesy of SCS GmbH & Co.

and Modems" sections in Appendix C for approved vendors.

Radio DIN Connections

The cable that is connected to the modem plug is an eight strand shielded wire. It seems like such a waste of four good wires but the truth is that you will only use four of these eight wires. Start by figuring out which four of the eight wires will be the ones that you will use. This should be found in your HF modem manual.

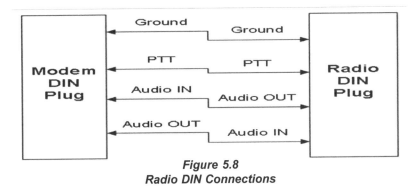

Figure 5.8
Radio DIN Connections

The four purposes or connections that you are looking for are called; ground, Push To Talk (PTT), Audio In and Audio Out. Go ahead and label these wires with a little sticker so you will remember what their names are. It's also helpful to draw a diagram in your log book for later reference and troubleshooting.

Next you need to look in your HF radio manual and find out what type of DIN plug you will need to use for the radio connection. On this DIN plug you will need to identify which lugs are for these same functions; ground, PTT, Audio In and Audio Out. Now comes the fun part! You will need to attach the ground wire from the modem to the ground on the radio DIN lug. Then you will attach the PTT wire of the modem to the PTT of the radio DIN lug. With me so far? Great!

Here's the part that gets everyone confused! The Audio IN wire from the modem needs to be connected to the Audio Out lug on the radio DIN plug. This makes sense if you think about it. What comes out of the radio must go INTO the modem. Finally, the Audio Out wire from the modem needs to be connected to the Audio IN lug on the radio DIN plug. What comes out of the modem must go INTO the radio! Got it? See with a little coaching you're turning into quite an electronics wizard!

The Anatomy Of A DIN Plug

For those of you that are adventurous we'll have a look at some basic information about DIN plugs; what they

Figure 5.9
8 Pin Male DIN

are, how they are numbered and how to get your modem and radio talking to each other! DIN stands for Deutch Industrial Norm. Now you've got one more piece of trivia for those happy hour games! These plugs come in various sizes and shapes. The pin sizes range from 5, 8 and 13 pins, they can be male or female and "mini." What's this male and female? The male DIN plugs are the ones that have the pointy ends that con-

nect into the equipment. The fe-male DIN plugs are the ones that have the holes that connect into the equipment. The connections to the HF radio will use a male DIN plug. The most common con-figuration will be an 8 or a 13 pin male DIN. See Figures 5.9 through 5.13 for examples of these plugs.

Figure 5.10
To Open Lift Here

All male DIN plugs are comprised of four parts: the outer plastic cover, two metal casings and the pins that are housed in a plastic mount. The two metal casings hold and secure the plastic mount with the pins and the outer plastic cover surrounds and holds the two metal casings. See Fig-ure 5.8 for an exploded view of a DIN plug.

To prepare a DIN plug for soldering you first have to remove the outer plastic cover. See Figure 5.10. Take a small, and I mean small flathead screwdriver and lift up gently on the plastic flap in the center of the outer plastic cover. While lifting up on this flap, grab the exposed metal at the tip of the plug and pull the metal tip out of the plastic casing. (Use your third hand for this maneuver). It should slide off easily.

Once the outer plastic casing is removed, the two metal casings should come apart and voila! You now have the pins exposed and ready to solder. Soldering a DIN plug is a definite art. If you have no experience soldering then I'd recommend you read up on it first. Check out the soldering references in Appendix A. While you're at it, you might also consider getting a bunch of extra DIN plugs. When you slather solder all over the pins and totally screw up the back of the plug you'll glad to have a fresh plug to begin anew. It's been my experience that DIN

Figure 5.11
DIN Exploded View

plugs are very flimsy. Keeping spares around is also highly recommended even if your system is not on a boat.

How To Read DIN Pin Numbers

A DIN plug has two sides: the side that plugs into the electronic equipment and the side that the cable wires are soldered to. So you don't get confused on which side is which, let's describe the two sides of the DIN plug. The side of the DIN plug that connects into the equipment will be referred to as the "equipment side" or pins of a DIN plug. See Figure 5.9. The side of the DIN plug that the wires are soldered to will be referred to as the "solder side" or lugs of a DIN plug. See Figure 5.9, 5.12 and 5.13. The numbers

Figure 5.12
8 Pin DIN Lug Numbering

of a DIN plug are often shown for the equipment side. Be sure that you are familiar with which view you are looking at. These pictures will help you keep on track when you try to identify the pin and the lug numbers. It's important to get these numbers correct so that you can be sure to solder the right wire to the right lug! The numbering shown in Figure 5.13 is from left to right. Note that the DIN numbering con-

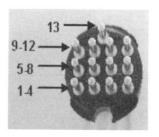

Figure 5.13
13 Pin DIN Lug Numbering

vention for Europe is different than in the USA--the examples I have used. Observing the actual pin out location of the plug will insure the correct wiring scheme regardless of the numbering scheme you are using!

Soldering Equipment

You'll need a soldering iron with a small tip, solder and something to hold the plug and the wires. I use a small, refillable butane soldering iron with a 1 millimeter pointed tip. See Figure 5.14. Soldering irons can be powered by butane, DC battery or AC current. They are available at Radio Shack, marine and hardware stores and HAM supply outlets.

Figure 5.14 Butane Soldering Iron
Courtesy of RadioShack

Always use rosin core solder with electronic equipment. Solder comes in many different diameters. The best size to use is the thinnest diameter you can find such as 0.032 inches. The smaller diameter rosin core solder melts quicker and requires less heat.

Unless you were born with four hands you will need something like the item in Figure 5.15 to hold the wire and the DIN plug while you solder them together. The "Extra Hands" also comes with a built in magnifying glass to help you get a close look at the tiny DIN lugs. I personally would like to see one with a microscope!

The Basics of Soldering

A good rule of thumb is to never begin a soldering project when you are tired or in a rush. You will be working with an extremely hot soldering iron that can get up to 1300 degrees Fahrenheit. To avoid getting burned you've got to have all of your wits about you.

Prepare the wires for soldering. You will need to remove about an eighth of an inch of the insulation. The easiest way to do

this is to use a cigarette lighter to heat the insulation. Apply the flame to all sides of the insulation for about three to five seconds. Allow the insulation to cool and then you can slide it right off the wire. You can also use a wire stripper if you like a real challenge. The small diameter wire requires a very gentle touch with a bulky wire stripper.

Figure 5.15 "Extra Hands"
Courtesy of RadioShack

Turn on and heat up your soldering iron to a low to medium setting. When the iron is hot, apply a small amount of solder to the tip of the soldering iron--this is called tinning. This is especially important to do if you have a new iron or a new tip that you are using for the first time. To clean the tip first tin the tip and then dab it on a damp sponge. Then reapply a small amount of solder to the tip. Next you will need to tin the wires and the DIN lugs. To do this, heat the individual wires for about three seconds with the soldering iron. While you're heating the wire, put the solder on the wire (not on the iron). When the wire warms up enough the solder will melt. Spread a small drop of solder on the wire. Heat the DIN lug with the iron and put the solder on the DIN lug (solder side pin). As the lug heats up the solder will melt. Apply a small drop of solder. Use caution here. If your iron is too hot, you will melt the plastic housing that holds the lugs. Avoid having any solder touch the adjacent lugs.

Finally, put the tinned wire onto the tinned lug and heat the DIN lug until the solder melts and a connection is made–about three seconds. Hold the soldering iron like a pencil taking care to only heat the desired lug. Don't move the wire until the solder has had a chance to cool. Soldering takes some practice. The more you practice, the better your skills will become. If you would like more information on the art and science of soldering, please see Appendix A under "Soldering."

Checking Continuity

When you're finished soldering or if you need to trouble-shoot your HF radio E-mail system you will need to check to be sure that you have successfully connected the DIN lugs to the wires. You are checking to be sure that the circuit is complete or has continuity. This is done using the continuity function of a volt meter.

The steps to check continuity include the following: First as-semble the DIN plug that you've finished soldering. Next, set your volt meter to the continuity function. Put one probe on the equip-ment side pin of the modem DIN and the other on the corre-sponding equipment side pin of the radio DIN plug. For example, put one probe on the PTT pin of the modem DIN plug and the other on the PTT pin of the radio DIN plug. Note that for this test it does not matter which probe on the voltmeter you use–the positive or negative.

Complete the testing on each of the four DIN pins you've just soldered. If all checks out then you are ready to plug in the radio and modem. If not, then it's back to the drawing board!

CHAPTER 6
SOFTWARE INSTALLATION

Each service provider has specific instructions for installing their software. Provider "Help" files are accessible after you have installed the software. These "Help" files will assist you with using the software. This chapter will give you some coaching regarding general software installation. I'll review where you can find the service providers' software and give you some configuration tips. Lastly, information on how to upgrade your SCS HF radio modem to the Pactor-3 mode will be discussed.

GENERAL INSTALLATION TIPS

You can obtain your service provider's software by either downloading it from their WEB site, from the enclosed "Idi-Yacht" CD ROM or a CD ROM that they provide. Software programs are constantly being updated. Check to be sure you have the most up to date version.

To get started you will need to copy the service provider's software and put it on your computer's hard drive. Determine a location where you will be able to easily find it such as: *c:/program files/serviceprovidersoftware*.

Once you have a copy of the software on your computer you are ready to install it. Before you install the software, be sure to read the directions! Close any programs that are running. Now find the provider's software on your computer and double click the install file. Follow the prompts that appear on your computer screen to complete the installation. When the software has been installed correctly you should see a message to that effect. If you receive any error messages during the installation, contact your service provider.

CONFIGURATION TIPS

Winlink 2000/AirMail

✓ **HAM Call Sign Entry**

You must enter your HAM call sign in the software program. The modem won't work if you miss this step! When you connect with the PMBO for the first time, you will be put on "probation" until the PMBO can check out the validity of your call sign. For new general class HAMs it may take a while for your upgraded call to be listed by the FCC.

✓ **Cable Connections**

Be sure all of your cables are hooked up! If necessary, review Chapter 5. When your cables are not properly configured then the modem will not work!

✓ **Setting The Audio Levels**

You must adjust the audio levels for the HF modem in the AirMail software. Levels that are too low will make your signal weak and unreadable. Levels that are too high will distort your transmissions. In either case, the net result is a poor or worse, no connection! See the AirMail Help files for more information. The instructions will walk you through the procedure.

✓ *Forwarding HF E-mail*

If you will be away from your radio for a period of time and wish to forward your AirMail messages to an Internet mail server--such as AOL, Netzero, Hotmail, Yahoo, etc.-- you can set this up in the AirMail Software. See the AirMail help file under "Options Message (Winlink 2000)" and read the instructions for "Alternate Address." Don't forget to turn this feature off when you return to the radio and make a connection to tell the system you don't want E-mail to be forwarded anymore! Also note that attachments will not be forwarded with this system. You must use the TelNet service to receive any attachments.

✓ ***Internet Access For HF E-mail***

You can access your AirMail messages through an Internet connection. File access with the WEB Browser is restricted to messages only--no attachments. Before you can do this, you must first obtain a password from one of the PMBO's. Send an E-mail to K4CJX or KN6KB and request a password. Once you have your password you can access the Winlink 2000 WEB page and get your messages. The WEB address to access your AirMail messages is: http://www.winlink.org/mail/mail.asp.

✓ **TelNet Services**

The TelNet system allows you to access your HF radio E-mail *and* attachments with an Internet connection. To enable this service you must set it up in the AirMail software. See the AirMail "Help Files" or the "Idi-Yacht" CD ROM under HF Radio E-mail Provider Software/AirMail for set up and access information.

MarineNet Wireless

✓ ***Dual MarineNet & HAM E-mail Operation***

If you wish to use both the Winlink/AirMail and the MarineNet Wireless systems you will need to make some adjustments in the AirMail software program settings in order for the AirMail program to work properly. Close the program after you have installed the MarineNet Wireless software. Open the AirMail program. Click on "Tools," and then "Connections." Set the baud rate to 38400. Next, click on "Advanced settings" and uncheck "Restore Modem Settings When Done" and uncheck "Reset Modem Before Initializing." Click "Close," "Apply," and then "OK." After you make these setting changes and you load your AirMail software, your modem should initialize properly.

✓ *Internet Access For HF E-mail*

You can access your MarineNet Wireless messages through an Internet connection. Go to their WEB site and click on "MarineNet Web Mail." You will be directed to another site that asks you for your account number, password and time zone. Enter the information and click "Log In." Remember that your account number and your password should be entered in lower case! Be aware that you are using your monthly minutes when you enter this site.

✓ *Free Signal Station Access*

To access the Free Signal mode you must install the software using a dial up networking configuration. See the MarineNet help files for more information.

SailMail/AirMail

✓ **Ship Station License**

You must enter your Ship's Station License into the software. If you forget to do this then the modem will not work!

✓ *Internet Access For HF E-mail*

You can access your SailMail messages through an Internet connection. Simply go to the SailMail WEB site that is located at; http://www.sailmail.com. Select the "Webmail" page, and then enter your user name and password.

✓ *Dual SailMail & HAM E-mail Operation*

If you want to use both AirMail and SailMail and haven't installed either program, go to the SailMail WEB page which is located at; http://www.siriuscyber.net/sailmail/ or use the version in the enclosed CD ROM. If you have already have installed the SailMail program and wish to add AirMail, go to the http://www.siriuscyber.net/sailmail/ WEB page and download the Ham version. Install the HAM version over the top of your current SailMail installation. It will leave your SailMail configuration and messages, but will add HAM capability.

PACTOR-3 UPGRADE

If you wish to upgrade to a modem to Pactor-3 mode or protocol you will need to purchase a SCS PTC-II, SCS PTC-IIe, SCS PTC-IIex or a SCS PTC-IIPro HF radio modem. You cannot upgrade any other brand of modem other than the SCS brand. Period!

The first step to achieve a Pactor-3 upgrade includes the following. You must pay SCS for the upgrade. As of this writing the cost of the upgrade is $149 (USD). It's important to note that the only way to directly pay SCS for the Pactor-3 upgrade is through the Internet. No phone calls, no letters and no pigeon couriers. The SCS company's WEB site address is found at http://www.scs-ptc.com. They do accept a variety of credit cards. The license number will be E-mailed to you within two business days. Some Commercial HF service providers will obtain the upgrade licensing for you. In that case, you pay the service provider and they pay SCS.

There are two options for obtaining a Pactor-3 license number; a "Serial Number license" option or a "MYCALL" license option. The

Made in Germany by SCS, Hanau
WWW.SCS-PTC.COM

OP10028102B04000E662CE

Figure 6.1
SCS Serial Number

first and preferred route is to upgrade using the "Serial Number license" option. This is accomplished by using the SCS modem's serial number. Look on the bottom side of the modem. You should see a grey tag with a bar code. The serial number is comprised of 16 numbers and letters and starts after OP1002 in the example provided in Figure 6.1. Note that with the SCS PTC-IIPro you can only use the Serial License upgrade option. The "Serial Number license" option upgrades the modem to Pactor-3 based upon the serial number of the modem. With the Serial Number license upgrade the modem isn't picky about which call sign(s) you use--it could care less. To access a service provider to send and receive E-mail you will still need a valid ship station license or valid HAM radio call sign or both. They are picky about these things and for good reasons!

If you do not see this serial number as illustrated in Figure 6.1, you either have a PTC-II or you have a PTC-IIe modem that was manufactured before 2002. Your options at this point are to upgrade by purchasing an electronic serial number for an additional $99 (USD) or to upgrade using the "MYCALL" license option.

The "MYCALL" license upgrade allows for the licensing of two valid call signs--a HAM and a ship station license or two HAM call signs. If you are a licensed HAM and plan to use both the HAM E-mail and Commercial E-mail system that's great. But if your first mate wants to use his or her HAM call sign on the HAM E-mail system along with your two call signs then that is not possible with a "MYCALL" license option. The upgraded Pactor-3 modem licensed with the MYCALL option looks for two call signs. If you try to use a call sign that is not one of the two listed in the license the modem will not work!

If you sell your boat then your ship station call sign (the one you will need to use commercial HF radio E-mail) will change. Ship station call signs are not transferable to a new boat--you will be issued a new one for the new boat. So, your new ship station license will not be valid in the modem and your old ship station license will not be valid! You will have to apply for a new "MYCALL" modem license from Germany that has the new ship stations license before the modem will work with your new call sign.

If you plan on becoming a HAM radio operator in the future and wish to use the Pactor-3 mode with a HAM radio HF E-mail provider in the future, you will have to change the "MYCALL" license of the modem to include your HAM call sign. In summary, the MYCALL license upgrade only includes two valid call signs for use with the modem. Any changes in call signs have to be done as an upgrade with the SCS company through the Internet. There is no charge to make this change.

For those only looking to use the HAM HF radio E-mail providers, you must have your HAM call sign. Please note that you can't use HAM HF radio E-mail until you have a General Class Amateur Radio Operator's license or higher. See Appendix D for more information on how to become a HAM radio operator.

The next step in the Pactor-3 upgrade process is to download the software that you will use to modify the HF radio modem. This can be done by visiting the SCS WEB site and obtaining the file that is specific for your type of HF modem or by downloading the specific file from the enclosed CD ROM. When you download this file to your computer, be sure to put it somewhere on your hard drive where you will be able to find it.

I recommend that you do not open this file with the Pactor-3 firmware upgrade until you have obtained your license number from SCS. If you do upgrade without the license number you will have a trial period of 20 Pactor connections after which your modem will stop working! If this happens you will have to reload the original firmware back into the modem to get it to come out of it's coma. This "original firmware" is located on the SCS WEB site and in the enclosed CD ROM because some of you may indeed make this mistake.

The final step in the Pactor-3 upgrade process involves the reprogramming of your SCS modem's software. With your HF modem license number from SCS at your side, connect your computer to the HF radio modem with the RS232 serial port cable (or the USB converter). Turn the computer and the HF radio modem on. Find the firmware file that you've downloaded and click to open it. Follow the prompts in the software and enter your SCS modem license exactly as shown--in upper case letters. You are now a Pactor-3 user!

The Pactor-3 operating mode has a new and different type of sound to it. It took me a while to get used to it. One of my first thoughts when I used it was that my radio had gone berserk and was spewing RFI! Do your blood pressure a favor and listen to the Pactor-3 sounds before you attempt a connection. Check out the enclosed "Idi-Yacht" CD ROM under "HF Digital Data Sounds" for a preview. Before you can listen to the sounds on the CD ROM you will need to have an audio player program on your computer. If you don't have an audio player, download the Real One Player that is located on the CD ROM.

It is important to note that after you upgrade your modem to Pactor-3, you will still have the capability to access a Pactor-1 and Pactor-2 connection--the upgrade doesn't lock you in to only using a Pactor-3 connection. Since Pactor-3 is about five times faster than a Pactor-2 connection it would behoove you to access the faster mode, where possible. Your batteries will thank you for that! As of this writing, only two service providers offer Pactor-3 mode exclusively. Others have all Pactor modes; 1 through 3 or 1 through 2. If your service provider offers all Pactor modes, they will have specific dial frequencies assigned for Pactor-3 connections and specific dial frequencies assigned for Pactor-1 and 2 connections.

SCS MODEM FIRMWARE UPGRADE

From the Winlink Development Team

July 25, 2003

At the suggestion of the USA Federal Communications Commission, changes have been incorporated into Airmail version 3.1.921 or greater and SCS firmware version 3.3c or greater which result in the dramatic improvements in user identification and interference reduction. We have more than satisfied their request to provide proper identification for our user community while drastically reducing the "blind calling" time of our users.

Because of the recent Airmail and SCS version revisions and our reduction of WL2K scan frequencies, the Winlink 2000 system has recently received praise from the USA FCC. Our agreed upon plan was to replace the old CW-ID with a screen readable FEC burst which identifies both the calling user and the called PMBO.

This has been accomplished for the SCS modems ONLY, but will soon be available for the remaining Pactor I modems supported by AirMail. We will alert those not using the SCS modem when the CW-ID replacement is available. Meanwhile, for those NOT using the SCS modem, please leave your CW-ID checked (on,) for, without it, you are NOT legally operating.

Realizing that Winlink 2000 is an International, Global system, with users from many different countries, the Winlink development team provides a common policy in keeping with virtually every country, including variations in frequency assignments, message content and proper identification. Because of the large percentage of users with US calls, we pay very close attention to the FCC rules regarding such matters.

HF RADIO E-MAIL FOR "IDI-YACHTS"®

In order to insure that the entire Winlink 2000 user community is on-board with these new software tools, which more than comply with virtually every Country's Amateur operating rules, we expect all SCS modem users to download and install both the new Airmail and SCS versions, turn off their CW-ID option and continue to enjoy the benefits of Winlink 2000.

Again, for those with the Pactor I only modems, shortly, a version of Airmail will be provided that will also identify in the FEC mode. For now, those NOT using the SCS modem should keep their CW-ID active.

Fortunately, most country's regulators have shown a relaxed attitude in recent years, and we expect this trend to continue as digital communications continue to grow. However, without the proper identification of the calling station which may be viewed by all, we cannot comply with any country's regulations, including the USA FCC. The new AirMail and Airmail/SCS firmware combination fulfills this void.

Please help us all to keep our service legal by updating as soon as possible! To update both AirMail and the SCS firmware, please use http://www.airmail2000.com. You will find it in the download section under the HAM version, Beta 3.1.921 and SCS version 3.3c.

-Your Winlink Development Team

Note that after you upgrade your modem to provide this CW identifier you will need to turn this function OFF!

If you haven't yet upgraded your firmware or you have a modem that does not yet have a firmware upgrade available, you will need to enable the CW identifier in the AirMail software program. To enable the CW identifier, click on Tools, Options, Connections and then Advanced Settings. You will see "Send Morse ID on Disconnect." Click that on. Insert 15 in the speed __ WPM or Words Per Minute box. Save your settings by clicking Close, Apply and Okay. You're done!

CHAPTER 7
USING HF RADIO E-MAIL

N ow you are on the threshold of using a new way to stay in touch with family, friends and business associates. You've put together a flawless HF radio system, selected and installed your HF

radio modem, set up an account with a service provider and installed their software on your computer. Don't let your excitement get in the way. Read on! This chapter will discuss common courtesy for using HF radio E-mail, HF propagation, how to use propagation tables, propagation software programs and outline the key steps to making a successful HF radio

Figure 7.1
Read The Book!

E-mail connection with a commercial and a HAM service provider.

If you had been raised in a radio family where you grew up around HF radios and electronics, this section would not be necessary. For those of you that haven't been exposed to this you'll be entering a whole new culture complete with new and mysterious terminology and equipment. Courtesy in any culture goes a long way--that is as long as you know how it's defined.

Common courtesy with your HF radio E-mail system begins with being sure that you understand what it is that you are doing! Be sure to read and understand the system before you attempt to use it. You must understand what frequencies you are licensed to transmit on and what frequencies you should be using to send and receive HF radio E-mail based upon the service provider that you have selected. Each of the service providers have their own unique and specific frequencies that you will dial into your radio to make an HF radio E-mail connection. Consult your service provider to obtain a list of these frequencies. If you have great difficulty installing and/or understanding the system, then be prepared to pay someone to assist you. Do yourself and your blood pressure a favor. Give yourself the time you need to install, learn and use the system before you dash off to the islands.

Listening For A Clear Frequency

One of the biggest mistakes that people make is to not listen to see if the frequency is occupied. The HF radio E-mail

Figure 7.2
Listen Up!

system is a one to a customer connection. You must be certain that the frequency is not in use. The frequencies that you will use for HF E-mail are reserved for digital transmissions only. It is very important to note that they are not exclusive to the Pactor mode! In the HAM bands, for example, you will need to listen for Pactor 1, 2 & 3 sounds *and* AMTOR, APRS, CLOVER, CW, GTOR, Packet, PSK31, RTTY and SSTV sounds. For the Marine SSB frequencies you will need to listen for CLOVER, RTTY and SITOR transmissions. *If you hear any of these digital modes being used on the frequency, you will have to wait until they are finished!*

Please insert the enclosed CD ROM into your computer and listen to these sounds. Be sure to load the Real One Software program on the CD ROM first so that you can play the sound files. Familiarize yourself with these sounds. Tune into an E-mail frequency and try and find these sounds for practice. If you start to transmit and you thought the frequency was clear and suddenly you hear some characteristic chirpings of Pactor or other digital sounds from another station in the background, then disconnect as quickly as you can. Sometimes signal fading can occur and fool you into thinking that the frequency is clear.

Timing Your HF E-mail Connections

In crowded harbors with other cruising boats be "Idi-Yacht" courteous. Plan your E-mail connections before and after Net times, Voice Weather and Weatherfax broadcasts. Your HF transmissions on any frequency will interfere with others nearby that are trying to listen to HF radio weather and traffic nets and cruisers that are trying to download a decent Weatherfax directly. Become alert and aware of when these nets and weather broadcasts occur.

I usually am up before the crack of dawn at 0500 and send my HF radio E-mail then. There are fewer folks trying to get on at that hour and I am not interfering with any nets, Weatherfax or voice weather broadcasts at that time (in my home port or usual cruising area). I guess now that my secret's out I'll have to get up earlier!

Frequency Selection

The frequency you have selected may actually be clear but you might not be able to connect. To understand how this can happen you need to realize that you are often trying to connect to a station that has one radio transceiver that scans a range of frequencies. As an example, let's pretend you've selected a commercial service provider called Charlie Whitefang. The Charlie Whitefang station in Florida lists four dial frequencies that you can use to make an HF radio E-mail connection. These dial frequencies can include the 2, 4, 5, 7, 8, 9, and 12 MHz frequencies. You decide you want to connect on the 4 MHz frequency that Whitefang lists as a dial frequency. You've listened closely for a few minutes and the dial frequency seems to be free and clear. You click the connect button on your software. All appears to be working properly with your HF radio E-mail system but you fail to connect. What's up?

If you tune into Charlie Whitefang's 8 MHz dial frequency and listen you probably will hear a station transmitting with those characteristic Pactor chirping sounds. What has happened is that the station you hear is using the Charlie Whitefang station on the 8 MHz frequency. So, even though the 4 MHz dial frequency is clear, the station is busy on the 8 MHz frequency. Remember HF radio E-mail is a one to a customer connection. If Charlie White-fang has only one radio at the station in Florida, only one E-mailing station can be connected regardless of how many frequencies are listed.

Radio Settings

For Pactor 1 &2 it is possible to use a 500 Hz filter. The addition of this filter helps squelch any noise on the frequency and helps keep a clean connection. For Pactor-3 it is not advised to use any filters so turn them off!
Be sure to turn off any or all audio processors. Consult your radio manual for more information. The speech compressor can distort the Pactor signal. If you have any noise or distortion, it will take longer to send and receive your E-mail or worse you may experience a "dropped call." A dropped call is where you connect and basically nothing happens. The station disconnects you after a preset time.

Be sure to turn off any noise blankers and notch filters. These devices can mute your reception. You want both your transmissions and reception to be crystal clear.

Another mistake folks make is to turn up the power on the radio to high and blast their way along the airwaves. Generally speaking, the best connection will be made with the smallest amount of power. If you can adjust your power, try connecting at about a third power. For those with a choice of either low or high power, try connecting at the low power setting. Using too much power is akin to screaming in someone's ear when you're on the telephone. Use only what's necessary and your connections will go through just fine. And besides, your batteries will thank you.

HF PROPAGATION

When you key the mike and transmit, be it voice or data, the radio converts the sound into radio waves. Radio waves travel at the speed of light; 300,000,000 meters per second. If all is working properly with your radio, these radio waves will travel in two directions; up and out to space--called skywaves--and along the earth's surface--called ground waves. Skywaves are where you get your long distance communications.

Figure 7.3
The Ionosphere Is A Mirror!

HF radio skywaves are influenced directly by the condition of the Ionosphere. The Ionosphere is a layer in the earth's atmosphere approximately 50 to 210 kilometers above the earth's surface. In the Ionosphere there are ionized gases that act as mirrors to reflect radio waves back to earth; hundreds if not thousands of miles from their point of origin. That is if conditions are optimal.

Radio waves have different lengths. The size or length of radio waves is controlled and changed by your HF radio transmitter. Low frequencies are long in length and high frequencies are short in length. Radio waves of different lengths act differently under varying atmospheric conditions. Let's take a look at some of the Marine SSB frequencies and their lengths of distance. The 2 MHz frequency is for short distances--with a range of approximately 50 to 200 miles (up to 1000 miles at night). The 4, 5 and 7 MHz frequencies are the intermediate frequencies--with a range of approximately 50-1500 miles. The

HF RADIO E-MAIL FOR "IDI-YACHTS"®

8 through 25 MHz frequencies are for long distance communications–with a range of approximately 500-7000 miles. As a general rule of thumb, the lower frequencies are better in the morning and the higher frequencies are better in the afternoon and evening. An easy way to remember this is: "The lower the sun–the lower the frequency. The higher the sun–the higher the frequency.

The sun is responsible for charging or ionizing these gases in the Ionosphere. Too much charging from the sun and the gases

Figure 7.4
Here Comes The Sun!

become sticky and hold onto your radio waves. If your radio waves are stuck in space you get nowhere with your radio transmissions! If there's not enough sun to charge these gases then your radio waves will not be reflected back to earth but will travel up, up and away to outer space. Be careful of what you transmit or in thirty years you may get a knock on your boat hull from some very confused aliens inquiring about the nature of those transmissions! If the gases in the Ionosphere are charged or ionized just right, then they will bend and reflect your transmitted radio waves back to earth hundreds if not thousands of miles from where they originated (your radio). Variables that can affect radio wave propagation in the Ionosphere include things like sunspots, solar flares and geomagnetic storms.

Ground waves or HF radio waves that travel along the earth's surface are also generated when you transmit. These type of radio waves explain why you can talk with or connect to stations that are only a short distance from where you are located when you're using the long distance frequencies.

Radio waves can be bent or diffracted by buildings, mountains, clouds, auroras and meteor trails which explains why sometimes you don't get the distance you expected with a particular frequency. Atmospheric noise and internal electrical noise can affect your ability to receive HF radio waves. To be successful with HF radio E-mail you must have both clear and strong reception as well as transmission. Refer to the "Idi-Yacht" CD ROM and Appendix A for more information on HF radio wave propagation.

HF Propagation Aids

You cannot connect to any service provider on all of their listed dial frequencies at any old time of the day or night. This is a very common mistake! There are software propagation programs and propagation charts and tables that can assist you in selecting the best frequency for an HF radio E-mail connection. All of these tools use time of day and distance to determine which frequency would be best to use for a connection. Propagation software programs can help you calculate the distance between you and the station you are trying to connect to. You input your latitude and longitude and the station's latitude and longitude and it will do the distance math for you.

The sun's effects on the Ionosphere are variable and not constant. Propagation charts and tables cannot take these variables into account. Software propagation programs can take these variables into account and can provide a more accurate projection of which frequency would be best at a given time of the day or night. Variables such as solar flares can make for a really bad day with HF radio E-mail and any HF transmission for that matter. Unless you have a way of updating your software program with the latest reports of solar activity you are not going to get the most accurate projection.

Most of us will do well with a simple propagation program that calculates the best frequency based on the time of day and the distance from the HF radio E-mail provider. If you are using a propagation program and you do not input the variables that can affect propagation, be prepared to occasionally fail to make a connection even though the propagation program says you're on the best frequency. Please note that AirMail and SailMail have an integrated propagation program in their software. If you are using one of the other service providers, you may need to use a separate propagation program or table to determine the best frequencies to use. See the "Idi-Yacht" CD ROM under HF Propagation Software for programs.

MAKING A CONNECTION

Commercial HF Radio E-mail Connections

First: Turn off any and all noise producing electronics. These can include your refrigerator, inverter, battery charger and the like. You should have run a check by now to know if there is something on your boat that produces noise on your HF radio. If you haven't been able to squelch the noise, then turn the offending device(s) off!

Second: Turn your radio, your computer, your GPS and your HF radio modem on and let them warm up. (You'll need GPS for your latitude and longitude to input your current position in your propagation software program). Be sure that your radio's squelch is turned all the way off or down. Turn off any narrow filters you may have connected to the radio.

Third: Check to be sure you have connected the computer to the HF modem and the radio to the HF modem. If in doubt about these connections, refer to Chapter 5.

Fourth: Open your service provider's software program. As you load up your service provider's software, you should see the HF radio modem flashing some red and green lights. If you are using SailMail you will need to click on the "Terminal" icon. When the software program has finished loading it should tell you that the modem initialized properly. If you get an error message at this point then turn to Chapter 10 and read the "Troubleshooting" section or consult your "Help Files." Now is the time to write your E-mails. Never write them when you are connected as it takes too much time.

Fifth: Check to be sure there are no Nets, Weather-fax or voice weather broadcasts going on. If so, try at a different time of the day!

Sixth: Determine which frequency would be best to use to make a connection by checking propagation. If you are using SailMail, you must first install the ITSHF program on your computer--see "Propagation Programs" in the enclosed CD ROM and load the ITSHF program. It's probably a good idea to restart you computer after you load this program. Once you've loaded the program onto your computer, it will appear magically within the SailMail software. You don't need to do anything more.

Next, be sure that you have entered your current latitude and longitude in the SailMail program. To do this click on "Tools" then "Options" then "Settings" and enter your position in the right hand corner of the screen. When you're done click on "Apply" and then click on "OK" which are both located at the bottom of the screen. Now you're ready to open the propagation program that is included in Sail-Mail.

In the SailMail program, click "View" and then click "Propagation." You should see a list on the left side of the screen of all the PMBOs. Once you're in the propagation screen, double click the station that you wish to connect to and check their propagation. You should see a colorful scale with percentages. Make a note of both the station and the frequencies that have the best percentage (i.e. 100%) and click the "X" in the top right corner of the screen to exit the propagation table. Note that the frequencies listed in the propagation table are not the ones you dial in!

If your service provider's software does not have an integrated propagation program, then click open your "external" propagation program or get out a propagation table or chart. Enter your latitude and longitude and the provider station's latitude and longitude. You need to determine what the best frequency is based on the distance from the station that you wish to connect to. Once you enter these numbers, the propagation program should give you a chart that shows you the frequencies that would be best to connect to that station. If you use a propagation chart or table, you will have to calculate the distance from the service provider and then look for the time of day on the chart to find the best frequencies.

Take a look at your service provider's list of frequencies. You may see their frequencies listed as "Center," and "Dial." The frequency you want to use is the "Dial" frequency. Enter this "Dial" frequency into your radio. Be sure to select the Upper Sideband (USB) mode on your HF radio--the radio should do this automatically for you.

Some commercial service providers transmit what they describe as a "ping" sound on their frequencies. If you have a service provider with this function, then all you should have to do is tune in to their listed dial frequencies and listen for the "ping" sound. If you hear it then the frequency you are on should provide a good connection. Did you notice the word should that I used in the last two sentences? Double check it with a propagation program or a chart!

Seventh: Turn your radio's power setting down to at least half; a third is probably best. If you don't have the option to make fine adjustments in your radio's power settings, then just turn your power down to "low." Listen to see whether or not the frequency is in use. If you are not sure what you are listening for please consult the enclosed CD ROM and listen to the characteristic chirping sounds that indicate the frequency is in use. Remember that this is a one to a customer connection.

Eighth: Okay! So you believe the frequency is the right one for the distance between you and the service provider's station and for the time of day. The dial frequency sounds clear. Hit the transmit icon in your provider's software program on your computer and you should see your radio begin to cycle between transmit and receive. When you make a connection you will see a message on the computer screen from the service provider acknowledging your connection. If you have no messages to send or receive, then the service provider will disconnect automatically. Congratulations on your first HF radio E-mail connection! If you don't see any of this happening, then go back to square one!

HAM HF Radio E-mail Connections

First: Turn off any and all noise producing electronics. These can include your refrigerator, inverter, battery charger and the like. You should have run a check by now to know if there is something on your boat that produces noise on your HF radio. If you haven't been able to squelch the noise, then turn the offending device(s) off!

Second: Turn your radio, your computer, your GPS and your HF radio modem on and let them warm up. (You'll need GPS for your latitude and longitude to input your current position in your propagation software program). Be sure that your radio's squelch is turned all the way off or down. Turn off any narrow filters you may have connected to the radio.

Third: Check to be sure you have connected the computer to the HF modem and the radio to the HF modem. If in doubt about these connections, refer to Chapter 5.

Fourth: Click open the AirMail software program. Now is the time to write your E-mails. Never write them when you are connected as it takes too much time. Next, click on the round "Terminal" icon. You should see the HF radio modem flash red and green lights. When the "Terminal" section of the AirMail program has finished loading it should tell you on the screen that the modem initialized properly. If you get an error message at this point then turn to Chapter 10 and read the "Troubleshooting" section or consult the AirMail help files.

Fifth: Check to be sure there are no Nets, Weatherfax or voice weather broadcasts going on. If so, try at a different time of the day!

Sixth: Determine which frequency would be best to use to make a connection by checking propagation. You must first install the ITSHF program on your computer—see "Propagation Programs" in the enclosed CD ROM and load the ITSHF program. It's probably a good idea to restart you computer after you load this program. Once you've loaded the program, it will appear magically within the AirMail software. You don't need to do anything more.

Next, be sure that you have entered your current latitude and longitude in the AirMail program. To do this click on "Tools" then "Options" then "Settings." Enter your latitude and longitude in the right hand corner of the screen underneath "Station Location." When you're done click on "Apply" and then click on "OK" which are both located at the bottom right of the screen. Now you're ready to open the propagation program that is included in AirMail.

In the AirMail program, click "View" and then click "Propagation." You should see a list on the left side of the screen of all the HAM PMBO stations. Once you're in the propagation screen, double click the station that you wish to connect to. You should see a colorful scale with percentages. Make a note of both the station and the frequencies that have the best percentage (i.e. 100%) and click the "X" in the top right corner of the screen to exit the propagation table. Note that the frequencies listed in the propagation table are not the ones you dial in!

Seventh: At the top and center of the AirMail Terminal screen you should see two drop down menus; the one on the left has the PMBO station call signs and the one on the right is a list of their Center frequencies. Click on the station's call sign that you want to use to make a connection. Next, click the right drop down menu and highlight and click the station's listed frequency that had the best propagation. You must check propagation each time before you attempt a connection as the time of day has a huge influence on which frequencies will be usable for a successful connection.

The frequency you want to tune the radio to is called a "Dial" frequency. Once you click on a station's frequency this "Dial" frequency will show up at the bottom of the AirMail Terminal screen. It will show "Dial freq=" and then list a frequency that is either USB or LSB. Enter this "Dial" frequency into your radio exactly as it appears. Be sure that your radio is on the correct mode–upper (USB) or lower (LSB) sideband–depending upon the frequency you've selected.

A common mistake that we all make is to try and connect to one PMBO using another PMBO's frequency. This often happens when you've had no luck connecting with one PMBO and so you impatiently click on another PMBO from the drop down menu and forget to change the dial frequency that is specific for the new PMBO in your radio! When you click "Connect" in this scenario you will not achieve a connection since you are calling a station that does not monitor the frequency you had previously dialed in! Oops! It's easy to make these small mistakes when you are half asleep and/or new to this system!

Eighth: Turn your radio's power setting down to at least half; a third is probably best. If you don't have the option to make fine adjustments in your radio's power settings, then just turn your power down to "low." Listen to see whether or not the frequency is in use. If you are not sure what you are listening for please consult the enclosed CD ROM and listen to the characteristic chirping sounds that indicate the frequency is in use. Remember that this is a one to a customer connection. If the frequency is in use and you start transmitting you could cause the station that is connected to lose their connection. That is not good Karma!

Ninth: Okay! So you believe the frequency is the right one for the distance between you and the AirMail PMBO's station and right for the time of day that you are attempting a connection. You've listened for a few minutes and the dial frequency sounds clear. Check that the "Handshake" icon is clicked on. This enables an automatic connect and disconnect function. The "Keyboard" icon requires you to manually type in a sort of secret code. Save that experience for later!

Click the green "Connect" icon in the top left of the AirMail Terminal program. Your radio will begin to cycle between transmit and receive. In a few minutes you should see a message on the computer screen from the PMBO acknowledging your connection. Your HF radio modem will be lighting up and blinking like a Christmas tree! If you have no messages to send or to receive, then the PMBO will disconnect automatically. Congratulations on your first HF radio E-mail connection!

CHAPTER 8
WEATHER & POSITION REPORTS

There is never enough weather information available when you are out on a boat cruising the "big blue." Having a variety of weather sources available to you can enhance both the safety and comfort of your voyage. The HF radio E-mail system can be used to download

several sources of weather forecasts. You can send position reports so that your curious family members can keep track of where you are. And when you are at sea you can send measured weather reports to meteorologists who will be eternally grateful for the information.

WEATHER DOWNLOADS

There are a wide variety of weather products that are available on the Internet and through your HF radio E-mail system. Some of these include the Offshore, High Seas, Tropical Cyclone & Coastal broadcasts, NAVTEX, Weather Fax Chart forecasts, satellite images and GRIB Weather forecasts. You can't directly surf the Internet using HF radio E-mail but you can access this information. These products can be indirectly downloaded from the Internet by requesting them from your service provider, by using the saildocs.com service or by sending an E-mail request to a NOAA FTP mail server.

Be aware that graphic weather files can be very large and take a while to download. In contrast, text weather files are generally short and easy to download. Check out the "Help File" in your provider's software for information on how to download weather products. Because some providers will charge you a fee for obtaining weather products it might be a good idea to learn to use the saildocs.com or NOAA FTP mail server method for obtaining weather information. Using either the saildocs.com or NOAA FTP mail server, weather products can be directly requested by E-mail so there are no service provider weather product fees to worry about. Requesting FTP mail files requires that you use a very strict format whereas saildocs.com is extremely simple and easy to use. Here are some examples of how you would request these weather products. To use saildocs.com simply send an E-mail:

```
TO:              query@saildocs.com
SUBJECT:         <blank>
MESSAGE:         send info
                 send index
```

This will provide you with information on how to access the products on this system and give you the index of Internet products available (mostly weather related) and the commands you will need to request what you want. Saildocs.com is a free service of Jim Corenman and the SailMail Association.

To use FTP mail to access the NWS/NOAA weather products, send an E-mail to: ftpmail@weather.noaa.gov. Put anything you like on the subject line. Enter a command script in the body of the message. NOTE: Correct capitalization for commands, directory and file names is critical. Below is an example of an FTPMAIL E-mail script:

```
TO:              ftpmail@weather.noaa.gov
SUBJECT:         Thanks a bunch for the info!
MESSAGE:         open
                 cd data
                 cd forecasts
                 cd marine
                 cd high_seas
                 get north_atlantic.txt
                 cd ..
                 cd offshore
                 get fznt25.knhc.off.n04.txt
                 cd /
                 cd fax
                 get PWEE11.TIF
                 get PYEE10.TIF
                 get PWEK11.TIF
                 get ftpmail.txt
                 quit
```

The FTP example requests the latest Atlantic high seas and Miami NAVTEX text forecasts; 24 hour Wind/Wave, 24 hour Tropical Surface and Tropical Cyclone Danger Area, Radiofax charts for the Gulf of Mexico and Tropical South Atlantic; and the latest FTP mail help file. Thanks to Tim Rulon at the National Weather Service for this information. Refer to the "Idi-Yacht" CD ROM file "FTPMAIL" for more information on how to use FTP mail servers to download weather products from the National Weather Service/NOAA. Or better yet, you can have a look at their WEB site: http://weather.noaa.gov/pub/fax/ftpmail.txt. Things change frequently so be sure to check back with the WEB site every so often. See Appendix D for NWS/NOAA weather product contact information.

I've also included an article by Gerry Boyd in the "Idi-Yacht" CD ROM that will give you with a wealth of information on how to use FTP E-mail servers for both weather products and for all sorts of other applications from ordering pizzas to looking up phone numbers! Another free source of E-mail based downloads include pagegetter.com at http://www.pagegetter.com

GRIB Weather Forecasts

GRIdded Binary data files (GRIB) are output files generated by computer forecasting models. The largest producer of GRIB weather is NOAA although other organizations such as the military and research institutions also generate GRIB files. NOAA GRIB files are generally the best ones suited for marine forecasts. GRIB files are generated four times daily. This frequency is expected to be increased sometime in the near future.

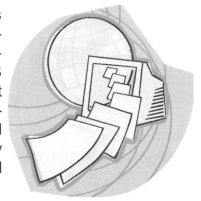

HF RADIO E-MAIL FOR "IDI-YACHTS"®

GRIB weather forecasts are available for the entire world and include air temperature, clouds, ocean current, rain, relative humidity, sea temperature, swell, swell+wind waves, wind speed and direction and wind waves that can be projected as far out as seven days. These forecasted parameters are animated over a chart. To view GRIB weather file forecast animations you will need to download these files and put them into a GRIB reader software program. This software program animates the file data over a chart for a period of up to seven days. See the "Idi-Yacht" CD ROM for GRIB reader software. There are two major types of GRIB weather files; those that are reviewed and edited by a meteorologist and those that display unedited computer generated model data. Beginning in the fall of 2003, edited GRIB forecasts became available for all of the NWS coastal products. The Offshore and High Seas edited GRIB weather forecasts are scheduled to be available sometime in the future.

It is imperative that you use the Pactor-3 mode to download these files. They can be very large and can take a long time to download with an HF radio E-mail system. Providers that have a 20K file download limit will provide GRIB files that include surface pressure, wind direction and speed for a three day period. Check your provider's help file for directions on requesting these files. Other sources of GRIB files that are free are available through saildocs.com and Global Marine Networks. See the previous discussion on "Weather Downloads" for information on saildocs.com. For information on accessing GRIB files with Global Marine Net, send an E-mail to: gmngrib@globalmarinenet.net and put the word "info" in the subject line. Note that unless you are using Windplot or MaxSea GRIB readers you will need to use a program to decompress these files. See the "Idi-Yacht" CD ROM under GRIB Readers for more information.

Never, ever rely solely on the computer generated, unedited computer model GRIB weather forecasts to plan your cruise. Rather, use them in conjunction with other weather forecast products that are available to you.

WEATHER BROADCAST PRODUCTS

Weather forecast products are broadcast over HF (High Frequency), MF (Medium Frequency) and marine VHF (Very High Frequency) radio at various times during the day. Voice forecast products include the Offshore and High Seas reports (which include the Tropical Cyclone reports), Tsunami and Ice reports and are broadcast on the HF bands. Offshore forecasts and storm warnings of interest to mariners are broadcast by USCG stations on the MF bands. Coastal weather reports are broadcast over marine VHF radio. You can receive these products directly as they are broadcast or you can use your HF radio E-mail system to download them from your service provider. There are no fees to listen to these transmissions. See the "Idi-Yacht" CD ROM under "WX Broadcast Products" for more information.

VOICE WEATHER FORECASTS

Offshore, High Seas, Tropical Cyclone, Tsunami, Ice & Coastal Reports

Static crashes and atmospheric noise can make listening to and copying these voice weather broadcasts very difficult if not impossible. It's a good idea to tape record these broadcasts so that you can replay garbled sections of the report and try to make sense out of it. Sometimes the transmission is so distorted that even a tape recorder doesn't help you copy it. Occasionally the broadcasts will  repeat old information and you may find yourself wondering what the latest position of that hurricane is that was headed your way. Another situation that you may find yourself in is that you are too far away to receive a coastal report on your marine VHF radio. When all else fails, you can use the HF radio E-mail system to download these forecasts.

RADIOFAX WEATHER FORECASTS

Weather Fax Charts & Satellite Images

Radiofax or Weather Fax forecast charts and satellite images are transmitted by stations all over the world. To tune into a Weather Fax frequency you will use Upper Sideband (USB). Subtract 1.9 kHz from the listed frequency to obtain the dial frequency. There are no fees for directly receiving these broadcasts. To access these charts and satellite images directly you will need either a dedicated weather fax receiver or a weather fax software program, a computer and an item called a demodulator. A demodulator is a device that converts radio signals to the ones and zeros of computer language so that your software program can display the broadcast information. Some software programs allow you to use your SCS PTC modem or a computer sound card as a demodulator.

See Appendix C for sources of Weather Fax software and the "Idi-Yacht" CD ROM for information on Weather Fax products, broadcast schedules, software and an example of Weather Fax radio sounds that you will be listening for. You can also obtain these products by using your HF radio E-mail system. Check your provider's "Help Files" for provider specific instructions.

DIGITAL WEATHER FORECASTS

Digital weather forecasts are text products that include NAVTEX and SITOR broadcasts. These transmissions are free of charge for anyone to receive. To access these broadcasts as they are transmitted you will need either a dedicated NAVTEX receiver, or a system comprised of a computer, a NAVTEX software program and a demodulator. Similar to Radiofax, some software programs allow you to use your SCS PTC modem or a computer sound card as a demodulator. Note that to receive the SITOR broadcasts you will use the NAVTEX software but the frequencies are different. See the "Idi-Yacht" CD ROM under "WX Broadcast Products" for more information. Consult your provider's software "Help Files" for information on how to request a download of these products.

NAVTEX

NAVTEX is an international automated MF (518 kHz) direct-printing service for navigational, meteorological warnings and forecasts and urgent marine safety information. It was developed to provide a low cost, simple, and automated means of receiving this information aboard ships within 200 nautical miles from shore. NAVTEX stations in the US are operated by the US Coast Guard.

There are no user fees associated with receiving these broadcasts. NAVTEX is a major element of the Global Marine and Distress Safety System (GMDSS). Ships greater than 300 gross tons and ocean going passenger vessels are required to monitor NAVTEX broadcasts. A NAVTEX software program is often included within the weather fax software program. These broadcasts can be received by tuning your radio (subtracting 1.4 kHz from 518) to 5.16.6 kHz on Upper Sideband (USB) or by adding 1.4 kHz and dialing in 519.4 kHz Lower Sideband (LSB). Trust me. If you tune your radio to 518 kHz using a NAVTEX software program you won't receive these broadcasts. A dedicated NAVTEX receiver will automatically adjust the frequency for you. See the "Idi-Yacht" CD ROM for software, broadcast locations, frequencies and times and for examples of what NAVTEX transmissions sound like. Refer to Appendix C for sources of NAVTEX software.

SITOR

Simplex Transmitted Over Radio or SITOR weather forecasts is a direct printing service for navigation that broadcasts High Seas Forecasts and storm warnings of interest to mariners. You can use the NAVTEX software program to receive these text broadcasts. To receive SITOR weather reports you will need to subtract 1.7 kHz from the listed broadcast frequency if you are using a software program to receive the transmission. See the "Idi-Yacht" CD ROM under WX Broadcast Products for more information, and under Digital Mode Sounds to listen to what a SITOR transmissions sounds like.

WEATHER REPORTING

Voluntary Observing Ship (VOS) Program

The United States VOS Program is organized for the purpose of obtaining weather and oceanographic observations from moving ships. An international program under World Meteorological Organization (WMO) auspices, the VOS program has forty nine countries as participants. The United States program is the largest in the world, with over 900 vessels and 16,000 reports per month. Vessels participating in the VOS program are active commercial vessels with licensed crew.

MAROB Program

The MAROB Program is an experimental voluntary marine observation program of the National Weather Service. It welcomes the participation of all mariners, both commercial and recreational, which are not part of the more in-depth VOS program. It is the goal of the program to collect as many marine observations from ships at sea as possible to improve the accuracy of coastal, offshore and high seas forecasts.

The MAROB program differs from the VOS Program in several ways. MAROB reports will be used by forecasters in the forecast decision process but these data will likely not be used directly by computer models. Any communications charges and the cost of any observing equipment will not be reimbursed by the Weather Service.

The National Weather Service is in the process of developing cooperative arrangements with organizations such as the United States Power Squadrons, the US Coast Guard Auxiliary, the Winlink 2000 Global Radio Network, the Maritime Mobile Service Network, Ocens, SailMail, SkyMate, MarineNet Wireless, and the YOTREP Reporting System to train observers and forward observations to NWS. Technologies utilized may include cellular and satellite telephone, HF Marine radio, MF Marine radio, VHF Marine Radio, Ham Radio, Webforms and E-mail. MAROB reporting schemes will work in conjunction with vessel position reporting systems such as Winlink's Position Reporter, the Maritime Mobile Service Network's ShipTrak, and the YOTREPs Reporter, to enhance the safety of mariners.

To find out how you can send weather reports and participate in this program, check your provider's "Help Files" or go to the URL for the latest information. The address is:
http://www.nws.noaa.gov/om/marine/marob.htm

POSITION REPORTS

Your relatives and friends can keep up with your current location when you send position reports through your service provider. Your latitude and longitude can be manually entered or you can attach a GPS to the HF radio modem and have it automatically input your position. These reports are uploaded to the Internet after you log on to your service provider.

The information on the Internet may list only your most recent position (Winlink & Maritime Mobile Service Net ShipTrak) or all of your position reports for the last thirty days (YOTREPS). Be sure to give your family and friends the call sign that you will use with your HF radio E-mail account. This will be either your HAM or your Ship Station call sign. Your family and friends will have to type in your call sign on the WEB page in order to find you!

Below are some Internet sites that offer position reports:

Pacific Seafarers Net reports:
http://www.bitwrangler.com/yotreps/

YOTREPS:
http://www.pangolin.co.nz/yotreps/reporter_list.php

Maritime Mobile Service Net ShipTrak:
http://mmsn.techmonkeys.net/

Winlink Position Reporter:
http://winlink.org/aprs/aprs.htm

Check the software "Help File" or with your service provider for the procedure you will use to send these reports and for the exact WEB site that they can be found on.

CHAPTER 9
FREQUENTLY ASKED
QUESTIONS

Questions always come up when you are using HF radio E-mail. The "Help Files" in your provider software program can probably help you with about 99% of all of your questions. This Chapter will attempt to list the most common questions that new HF E-mailers have. Answers will be provided or the reader will be directed to another source for information.

COMPUTER SETUP

My computer does not have a serial port. How do I connect the HF modem to it?

You will need to purchase a USB to Serial Port Converter to make this connection. See Chapter 5 under "USB to Serial Port Converters" for information. See Appendix C under "USB to Serial Port Converters" and Marine SSB Radio Systems & Modems" for sources of this item.

CONNECTING TO A SERVICE PROVIDER

Can I surf the Internet with HF radio E-mail?

No. If you need to surf the Internet you should consider purchasing a satellite phone or plan on visiting an Internet cafe.

Where do I find the latest version of my service provider's software?

Look at your service provider's WEB site. Most providers have their software available for download. See Appendix B for contact information.

Which frequencies do I use to send E-mail through my HF radio modem?

You will need to set up an account with a service provider. There are specific frequencies that are unique for each of the service providers' stations. Contact your service provider for a current list.

I see Mark, Space, Center and Dial Frequencies listed by my provider. Which one do I dial into the radio to make a connection?

You will enter the listed "dial" frequency into your radio to make an HF radio E-mail connection.

How do I determine which of my provider stations and which of their frequencies to use to send and receive my E-mail?

Generally speaking, the correct frequencies for connections to the service provider stations will depend upon how far you are from them and what time of the day it is. Use a propagation software program to help you determine which frequency and which station would be best to connect to. See the enclosed "Idi-Yacht" CD ROM for propagation software.

What's the difference between a frequency scanning and a free signal system?

In a frequency scanning system, the service provider uses one HF radio to scan multiple frequencies. In a free signal system, the service provider uses one HF radio per frequency.

How will I know when a frequency is in use/busy?

In a frequency scanning system, you will hear the characteristic chirping sounds of a Pactor transmission. In a free signal system you will *not* hear the characteristic free signal sounds. You may hear the characteristic Pactor chirping sounds if the frequency is in use. When you try and connect to this system a Pactor-3 modem won't allow it. The software program will tell you that the frequency is busy. See the "Idi-Yacht" CD ROM for examples of these sounds.

Can I access my HF Radio E-mail from the Internet?

Yes you can. See Chapter 4 or consult your software program's "Help File" for provider specific information on how to do this.

Do I need to transmit on full power to connect to my service provider?

No. In fact transmitting on full power is usually not a good idea. You should always try and connect at the lowest power necessary to make a connection. Try starting at a low power setting and work your way up if your radio has the option of adjusting the power output.

What will my HF radio E-mail address be?

For HAM radio it will be yourhamcallsign@winlink.org. For the commercial providers, see Chapter 4 under the specific provider for more information.

EQUIPMENT PURCHASE/INSTALLATION

Where can I find someone to install my system?

There is an extensive list of HF radio and modem vendors in Appendix C under "Marine SSB Radio Systems & Modems."

Where can I purchase an HF Radio and/or an HF radio Modem?

See Appendix C under "Marine SSB Radio Systems & Modems" for vendors in your area.

HF ANTENNA SETUP

What are my options for an HF antenna on my boat?

You can use part of the standing rigging such as the backstay on a sailboat. Or you can install a 23 or a 17 foot 6 inch SSB whip. See Chapter 2, Appendix A and the "Idi-Yacht" CD ROM for more information.

HF MODEM SETUP

Where can I buy the cable with the DIN plugs to connect my modem to the radio?

You can buy ready made cables from a variety of sources. See Appendix C under "HF Modem to Radio DIN Cables" and "Marine SSB Radio Systems & Modems" for vendors.

How do I upgrade my SCS modem to a Pactor-3?

Your service provider can assist you with this or you can purchase the software upgrade directly from SCS on the Internet; http://www.scs-ptc.com. See also Chapter 6 for information and step by step instructions.

HF RADIO SETUP

The manufacturer says that my radio is "E-mail ready." So I don't have to buy an HF modem?

You have to buy an HF modem. "E-mail ready" means that the radio is capable of rapid switching from transmit to receive and is capable of continuous duty for a minute or two. It also means that some of the E-mail frequencies have been preprogramed into the memory channels. Get your credit card ready!

Where can I purchase RF/Toroids/Chokes?

See Appendix C under "Radio Frequency Interference."

Where can I find copper mesh?

See Appendix C under "Copper Mesh/Strap/Screen" and "Marine SSB Radio Systems & Modems" for vendor information.

I bought copper foil with a 0.001" thickness to make my groundplane. Is this okay?

Not for a permanent installation. Copper foil with a 0.001 inch thickness is extremely thin--about the thickness of aluminum foil. It won't last very long as it is subject to corrosion in the saltwater environment. Where possible, you should use copper strap that is 4-6 inches wide and about 0.013 inches thick. Remember that it is surface area that you are concerned with. The thicker the copper strap the greater the surface area.

What is a line isolator and how do I install one?

A line isolator is a series of five RF chokes that is enclosed in a plastic tube. It is installed in-between the radio and the tuner as close to the tuner as you can get it. See Appendix C under "Radio Frequency Interference" for sources of a line isolator.

What size fuse should I use for my HF radio?

Generally, a 30 amp in-line fuse on the positive wire close to the battery will do the job. Some folks recommend installing an in-line fuse on the negative side as well. Check your manual for your specific radio requirements.

LICENSING--HAM

What's the difference between HAM and Marine SSB radio?

Both systems use Single Sideband radio. The differences are in the licensing requirements and the frequencies that are allocated to be used with each system.

What licenses do I need to transmit E-mail through the HAM Amateur Radio service?

You will need a General class Amateur radio license to use the HAM Winlink E-mail system.

What are the latest requirements to become a General class HAM radio operator so that I can use the Winlink system?

Two written tests and a five word per minute Morse code test are all you need to become a General class HAM radio operator. See Appendix D for contact information.

How do I find out where HAM exams are held?

In the US, contact the American Radio Relay League (ARRL) or W5YI. Outside the US you can contact the International Amateur Radio Union (IARU). See Appendix D or the enclosed CD ROM for contact information specific to each Country.

LICENSING--MARINE SSB

What licenses do I need to transmit E-mail through the commercial service?

In the US you will need two licenses; a ships station license and a restricted radio operator permit. See Appendix D for US and other Country licensing information.

How do I get a ships station license?

In the US the FCC issues this license. There are no tests to take--just a fee to pay. See Appendix D for the FCC and other Country licensing sources and requirements.

How do I get a restricted radio operator permit?

In the US the FCC issues this license. Again there is no test to take--just a fee to pay. See Appendix D.

TECHNICAL ASSISTANCE

Where can I get technical support?

Contact your service provider for help with software related issues, see Appendix B. For hardware issues, contact the distributor where you purchased the equipment.

Where can I find a seminar or a course to teach me how to set up and use my radio and/or my HF E-mail system?

Check out the author's WEB site for dates, times, locations and fees; http://www.idiyachts.com.

PACTOR MODES

What do Pactor transmissions sound like?

See the enclosed "Idi-Yacht" CD ROM under "HF Radio Data Sounds" to listen to some examples. This requires an audio player program such as RealOne. You can download the RealOne player from the "Idi-Yacht" CD ROM which is located under "Download these Files First!"

What modems are available for Pactor mode E-mail?

See Chapter 3 for a list of compatible modems and their prices as of September 2003.

What is the speed of Pactor-1?

A net data rate maximum of 200 bits per second.

What is the speed of Pactor-2?

A net data rate maximum of 800 bits per second.

What is the speed of Pactor-3?

A net data rate maximum of 2800 bits per second.

POSITION REPORTING

How do I send a position report?

Check the "Help File" in your software program for your specific service provider's procedures. See Chapter 8.

How does my family view my location on the Internet?

Your family and friends will need to know the call sign that you will be using when you submit your position report. For the Winlink system it will be your HAM call sign. For the commercial providers it will be your ship station license. Check the "Help File" in your software program or with your service provider regarding the exact WEB site that your position reports will be posted on.

WEATHER DOWNLOADS

What are GRIB weather files?

GRIdded Binary data files (GRIB) are output files generated by computer forecasting models. Human forecasters do not review the data before it's published and therefore some knowledge and awareness is required by the end user. See Chapter 10 for more information.

What is a GRIB Reader?

A GRIB reader is a software program that enables you to animate GRIB weather forecast data. There are a variety of these programs available--some are freeware or demos and others are available for purchase. See the "Idi-Yacht" CD ROM for GRIB Weather Readers.

How do I download GRIB weather files?

You request these files from you service provider. Check with your service provider for their procedures and any additional fees.

How do I use my HF radio modem to receive Weather Faxes & NAVTEX broadcasts?

If you have a SCS-PTCIIe, Ilex or Pro you can use software that will allow you to receive Weather Fax forecasts and NAVTEX broadcasts directly through your HF radio modem. See Appendix C under "Weather Fax Software" for programs that are compatible with the SCS modems and the "Idi-Yacht" CD ROM for software.

You can download Weather Fax forecasts, GOES satellite images and NAVTEX files from most of the HF E-mail service providers. These are generally very large files that will take a while to download. Be aware that some providers charge a fee for attachments. It is much more economical to receive them directly using a software program.

How do I use my HF radio modem to receive text weather reports such as Tropical Storm/Hurricane updates, Offshore and High Seas Reports?

You can download these files from most of the HF E-mail service providers. Check your software program's "Help File" for your provider's instructions. Be aware that some providers charge a fee for this information.

WEATHER REPORTING

How do I send a weather report?

This is for measured weather data from ships at sea only! Check your software's "Help File" for specific information on how to send a weather report through your service provider. See Chapter 8 and the "Idi-Yacht" CD ROM for more information .

HF RADIO E-MAIL FOR "IDI-YACHTS"®
NOTES:

_____

_____

_____

_____

_____

_____

_____

_____

_____

_____

_____

_____

_____

_____

_____

CHAPTER 10
TROUBLESHOOTING

This Chapter will list some common problems that HF radio E-mail users encounter. It is not intended to be a comprehensive guide for troubleshooting all of the HF modems, radios and service provider's software. Check the troubleshooting section of your HF modem, radio and service provider's software for specific information related to your system. If all else fails you may have to find someone to come out and have a look at your system for some hands on troubleshooting. Don't despair! You can get the problems fixed! See Appendix C for installation experts.

I can't connect to my service provider.

Correct Frequency?

☆ Check that you're using the correct frequency. There are center, space, mark and dial frequencies that can be listed for the station you are trying to connect. Be sure you are using the *dial* frequency. If you are using the Winlink system be sure that you are on the correct sideband setting (i.e.) Upper or Lower Sideband. Note that all commercial connections will be on Upper Sideband (USB).

Right Connections?

☆ Check all of your connections. Are the radio and modem turned on and connected to each other? Is the modem and the radio connection good? DIN plugs are notoriously flimsy--check continuity of the cable. See Chapter 5.

HF RADIO E-MAIL FOR "IDI-YACHTS"®

Is The Radio Transmitting?

✫ Check the radio's power output with an RF watt meter or use the forward power meter on your radio if it has one. Or try and get a voice radio check on a hailing frequency. This will tell you the strength of your transmissions and if you are on or off frequency. Check the tuner and antenna connections for corrosion and clean if necessary.

Too Much Electrical Noise?

✫ Is your reception distorted and noisy? Be sure to turn off all noise producing electronics before you try and connect.

Too Much Standing Wave Ratio (SWR)?

✫ The lower the SWR the better the match between the antenna and the transmitter. Ideally the SWR should be below 3:1. With a high SWR much of the transmitted signal is reflected back down the transmission line to the radio and not up to space. With a high SWR the radio will reduce it's transmitted or forward power to protect itself from damage. High SWR generally means there is a problem with the antenna. Check for corrosion on the antenna and tuner connections. Other sources of trouble could be your tuner, your radio or both!

Right Frequency For Time Of Day and Distance?

✫ Are you using the best frequency for the distance and time of day that you are trying to connect? Consult a propagation table. Remember that solar flares and geomagnetic storms will interfere with HF communication and can be the source of the problem. Local noise from radio stations and noise from electric power lines can also interfere with HF E-mail connections.

Station Down For Maintenance?

✯ The service provider's station may be down for some reason. There may be a lightening storm moving through the area or the station is undergoing repairs and maintenance.

Frequency In Use?

✯ If your provider uses frequency scanning, the station may be busy on another frequency. It is possible that the station is busy and you can't hear the other station that is connected. Try another station or try again at a different time.

Batteries Charged Up?

✯ Check your battery voltage. If the batteries are low this will cause distortion of your transmissions and make it impossible to connect.

Radio Noise Blankers and Filters Turned Off?

✯ For the Icom M-710 and M-700Pro be sure that the "clarity knob" is set at the center! For the Icom 718, center the "RIT-Shift" knob! For Pactor-3 mode you should have your filters turned off!

My computer screen freezes up when I transmit.

Source Of The Radio Frequency Interference (RFI)?

✯ This problem is usually the result of RFI. The computer may actually be the culprit. Tune an AM radio to a crystal clear station and bring it close to the computer. If the AM station crackles with static then you've made your diagnosis. Move your computer as far away from the HF radio and modem as possible and this should fix the problem. You can try adding more RF chokes and/or a line isolator.

Groundplane Adequate?

✭   Double check your HF radio set up—especially the ground-plane. Try adding more copper strap or mesh.

I get a "dirty connect" message from the service provider and keep getting disconnected.

Get Rid Of The Noise!

✭   There is too much noise on your signal. Be sure to turn off your inverter, shore power, refrigerator and any other electrical items that might cause noise. Start with turning everything off and listen for noise. See the "Idi-Yacht" CD ROM for examples. If you think you've got everything off and you hear noise there is something that you've missed or something nearby causing the problem. An adjacent boat's generator, or refrigerator or the marina's transformer could be the culprit!

I hear noise through my stereo speakers when I transmit on certain frequencies.

✭   Check your groundplane connections--add more copper strap or mesh.

✭   Add more HF chokes on the cable from the radio to the antenna tuner, on the cable to and from the radio modem and the HF radio. Consider installing a line isolator.

✭   If you have the length, try looping the INSULATED positive and negative power wires at the HF radio to about five turns. This is called a "poor man's choke."

✭   Route your power connections for the HF radio directly to the battery. Use oversized wires for the run. Don't forget to put an in-line fuse close to the battery on both the positive and negative wires.

I can't connect on the higher frequencies.

✶ Check propagation. Are you trying to connect at the right time of the day based upon the distance between you and the service provider? A good rule of thumb is the higher the sun, the higher the frequency. The lower the sun, the lower the frequency.

✶ Your radio may not be transmitting properly. Check the SWR and the forward output power for problems.

The modem will not initialize.

✶ Check the continuity of your modem to radio cable. The vibration of the boat and/or poor soldering can cause the soldered joints to come apart.

✶ Double check that you have connected the Audio In pin from the radio to the Audio Out pin to the modem and the Audio In pin from the modem to the Audio Out pin from the radio. This is a very common mistake!

✶ Try turning off the modem and rebooting the software program.

✶ Sometimes HF modems can be temperamental. You will have to go into the modem and perform a reset. See your modem manual for details.

The modem will not turn on.

✶ Check to see that the power connections are properly set up. The center prong on the power connector is usually positive. Check the in-line fuse to see if it's blown. Check your connections with a volt meter to see if you have power going to the modem. If all else fails, check your manual and look for a fuse that might be located on the inside of the modem (unlikely but possible).

I have to remove the DIN plug from the radio or my voice transmissions are garbled.

You may need to disconnect the cable from the radio to the HF modem. This can be done with an HF modem switch.

✯   A modem Off/On switch is essentially a break in the cable that connects the radio modem to the HF radio. This prevents you from having to plug and unplug the DIN plug from the HF radio. Figure 10.1 illustrates such a switch. Note the ferrite chokes on the cable aft of the DIN plugs. A modem switch is a device that allows you to disconnect the modem from the radio without unplugging the DIN plug from the ra-dio. This is important for two

Figure 10.1
Off/On Modem Switch
Courtesy of Ted Gimble, N1XVR

reasons. First, DIN plugs are pretty flimsy and continued unplugging and plugging them in can wear them out pre-maturely. Second, with some HF radios your voice trans-missions will be garbled if you don't unplug the modem from the radio. Radio waves will travel through your cable connection from the HF radio to the radio modem and dis-tort your transmissions even if the HF modem is turned off.

✯   Depending on your HF radio installation, you may not be able to access the back of the radio without remov-ing a gazillion things and putting your body through what I call the "Jamaican rubber person contortion." Do yourself a favor and plan to make up an off/on switch. This switch is easy to make and will cost you about $10 (USD). See the "Idi-Yacht" CD ROM under "HF Modem Switch" for parts and information.

APPENDIX A
REFERENCES

Antennas

Alvis, J.E. & Britain, K.E. *Antennas. Selection, Installation and Projects.*
Master Publishing, Inc., Richardson, Texas, 1994

Jones, P. *Wirebook IV.*
© 2002, The Wireman, Inc.
http://www.thewireman.com

Johnston, J. *"Cruising with ham radio--an antenna alternative.* Southwinds Magazine, July 99.

Moxon, L. *HF Antennas for All Locations.*
© 1989, Radio Society of Great Britain

Straw, D. (Ed.) *The ARRL Antenna Book.*
© 2000-2002, The American Radio Relay League, Inc.
ISBN: 0-87259-804-7

Thompson, J. *Frequently Asked Questions About Antenna Systems and Baluns plus Exploring Popular Antenna Myths…and the Problem with Inverted V Antennas.*
Portsmouth, VA,1999.

Antenna Tuners/Couplers

Parise, J. *"QST Reviews Five High-Power Antenna Tuners."*
QST Magazine, February 2003, pp. 69-75.

AirMail/SailMail Software Set Up

Jensen, G. *The Sailor's Quick-Start Guide To AirMail/ SailMail/Winlink 2000.* ©2002

Electrical Continuity Checks

Evans, A. J. *Using Your Meter. VOM and DVM Multitesters.*
Master Publishing, Inc., Lincolnwood, Illinois. Second Edition, ©1994.

Electrical Noise Suppression

Beyn, E.J. *The 12 Volt Doctor's Practical Handbook for the boat's electrical system.*
C. Plath North American Division, Annapolis, 1983.

Calder, N. *Boatowner's Mechanical and Electrical Manual. How to Maintain, Repair, and Improve Your Boat's Essential Systems.*
International Marine, Camden, Maine, 1996.

Carr, J. J. *Practical Radio Frequency Test & Measurement— A Technician's Handbook*
© 1999, Newnes.

Miller, C., and Maloney, E. S. *Your Boat's Electrical System. Manual of Electrical and Electronic Projects.*
Second Edition, Hearst Marine Books, New York, 1988.

Electrical Wiring

Brotherton, M. *The 12 Volt Bible For Boats.*
Seven Seas Press/International Marine, Camden, ME, 1985.

Calder, N. *Boatowner's Mechanical and Electrical Manual. How to Maintain, Repair, and Improve Your Boat's Essential Systems.*
Second Edition, International Marine, Camden, Maine, 1996.

Jeffrey, K. *Independent Energy Guide—Electrical Power for Home, Boat & RV.*
Orwell Cove Press. © 1995 Kevin Jeffrey.

Payne, J. C. *The Marine Electrical and Electronics Bible. A Practical Handbook for Cruising Sailors.*
Grafton Books; 2nd Edition, October 1998.

Snead, D., and Ishihara, R. *Living On 12 Volts With Ample Power.*
Ample Power, Revised Edition, 1998.
http://www.amplepower.com

Snead, D., and Ishihara, R. *Wiring 12 Volts For Ample Power.*
Ample Power, Revised Edition, 1995.
http://www.amplepower.com

HAM Operating Modes

Arland, R. *ARRL's Low Power Communication—The Art and Science of QRP*
© 1999, The American Radio Relay League.

Davidoff, M. *The Radio Amateur's Satellite Handbook*
Revised First edition, 3rd printing, © 1998-2001, The American Radio Relay League.

Harris, M. *Communications at Sea. Marine radio, e-mail, satellite and Internet services.*
Sheridan House, Inc., New York. ©2003 M. Harris.

Ford, S. *ARRL's HF Digital Handbook.*
© 2001, The American Radio Relay League, Inc.

Horzepa, S. *APRS Tracks, Maps and Mobiles. A Guide to the Automatic Position Reporting System.* © 1999, The American Radio Relay League, Inc.

Taggart, Dr. R. *The ARRL Image Communications Handbook* © 2002, The American Radio Relay League

Comprehensive information on HAM operating modes.
http://www.ac6v.com/opmodes.htm

Extensive links to information regarding HAM operating modes.
http://www.dxzone.com/catalog/Operating_Modes/

Extensive information regarding HAM digital operating modes from NB6Z.
http://home.teleport.com/~nb6z/frame.htm

More links including a live demonstration of the Internet Radio Linking Project (IRLP) where 2 Meter HAM repeaters are linked to the Internet.
http://www.eham.net/newham/modes

"Packet Radio Primer" http://www.choisser.com/packet/

There are numerous other sites. I recommend that you pull up http://www.google.com and do a search for HAM radio operating modes. Good surfing!

HF Radio Installation

Calder, N. *Boatowner's Mechanical and Electrical Manual. How to Maintain, Repair, and Improve Your Boat's Essential Systems.* Second Edition, International Marine, Camden, Maine, 1996.

Harris, M. *A Guide to Small Boat Radio* Sheridan House, 1991.

HF Radio Modification

Extensive listing of modifications for HF radios.
http://www.mods.dk/index.htm

HF Radio Propagation

Jacobs, G., et al. *The New Shortwave Propagation Handbook.*
© 1995, CQ Communications Inc. ISBN: 0-94301-611-8

Learn To Use The Computer

Rathbone, A. *Microsoft® Windows XP for Dummies®*
John Wiley & Sons; September 2001. ISBN: 0764508938

Rathbone, A. *Windows ME for Dummies®*
John Wiley & Sons; July 2000. ISBN: 0-76450-735-4

Rathbone, A. *Windows 98 for Dummies®*
John Wiley & Sons; 1st Edition, June 5, 1998.
ISBN: 0-76450-261-1

Learn To Use Marine SSB Radio

Brown, Capt. M. *Marine SSB Radio For "Idi-Yachts"® A Guide For Using Marine Single Sideband Radio While Cruising The Bahamas, Cuba, Florida & The Eastern Gulf of Mexico.*
Cruising Companion Publications, Marathon, Florida, 2002.

Marine SSB Licensing-- Australia & Pacific

The Penta Marine Radio Communications Manual
Second edition, Penta Marine Radio Communications.
ISBN: 0-646-31079-8
http://www.pentacomstat.com.au/

Marine SSB Licensing --Canada

WEB: http://strategis.ic.gc.ca/engdoc/main.html

Marine SSB Licensing--USA

West, G. *"The Marine Radio License Application Process. Filing Electronically with the FCC."*
http://www.shakespeare-marine.com/new-fcc-license-steps

Radio Frequency Interference (RFI)

Corenman, J. *AirMail® Primer.*
http://www.airmail2000.com

Hare, E., et al. *The ARRL RFI Book— Practical Cures for Radio Frequency Interference.*
© 1998, The American Radio Relay League, Inc.
ISBN: 0-87259-683-4

Soldering

"A Soldering Tutorial For the Mechanically Challenged."
http://www.kingbass.com/soldering101.html

Brewster, R. *The Art of Soldering*
Babani Electronics Books BP324. ISBN: 0-85934-324-3

Singman, A. *Modern Electronic Soldering Techniques.*
Sams Technical Publishing. ISBN: 0-7901-199-6

"The Art of Soldering." February 2001, QST Magazine,
© 2001 The American Radio Relay League, Inc.
http://www.arrl.org/tis/info/pdf/0102072.pdf

Weather

Goldstein, M. *The Complete Idiot's Guide To The Weather.*
The Penguin Group, 1999.

Hodgson, M. *Basic Essentials: Weather Forecasting.*
Globe Pequot Press, 1999.

Williams, J. *The Weather Book.*
Random House, Inc., 1997.

Weather Fax

"A Beginners Guide To Understanding Weather Fax"
http://www.hffax.de/Beginners_Guide/beginners_guide.html

Carr, M. W. *International Marine's Weather Predicting Simplified: How to Read Weather Charts and Satellite Images.*
International Marine/Ragged Mountain Press, 1999
ISBN: 0-07012-031-5

Dashew, L., and Dashew S. *Mariner's Weather Handbook.*
1998.

Harris, M. *Understanding Weatherfax*
Sheridan House, 1997.

Weather Satellites

Taggart, R. *Weather Satellite Handbook*
Fifth edition, 2001 American Radio Relay League, Inc.

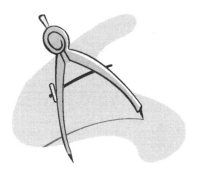

HF RADIO E-MAIL FOR "IDI-YACHTS"®
NOTES:

_____

_____

_____

_____

_____

_____

_____

_____

_____

_____

_____

_____

_____

_____

_____

APPENDIX B
HF E-MAIL SERVICE PROVIDERS

HAM Radio

Winlink 2000, Steve Waterman, K4CJX
http://www.airmail2000.com
E-mail: K4CJX@comcast.net or K4CJX@winlink.org

Commercial

MarineNet Wireless, John Heron
17940 Loxahatchee River Rd., Jupiter, FL 33458
Phone: 561-747-5686   Fax: 561-747-9357
http://www.marinenet.net   E-mail: Info@marinenet.net

SailMail Association, Jim Corenman and Stan Honey
912 E. Charleston Rd., Palo Alto, CA 94303
Phone: 619-980-6215   Fax: 650-856-1638
http://www.sailmail.com   E-Mail: sysop@sailmail.com

Sea Wave, LLC
76 Hammarlund Way Middleton, RI 0284
Phone: 401-846-8403
http://www.seawave.com   E-mail: info@seawave.com

ShipCom, LLC, Rene Stiegler
7700 Rinla Ave., Mobile, AL 36619
Phone: 251-666-5110
http://www.wloradio.com   E-mail: info@wloradio.com

HF RADIO E-MAIL FOR "IDI-YACHTS"®
NOTES:

_____

_____

_____

_____

_____

_____

_____

_____

_____

_____

_____

_____

_____

_____

_____

APPENDIX C
EQUIPMENT & SERVICES

BACKSTAY/STANDING RIGGING ISOLATORS

Sta-lok®
Sta-lok Terminals Ltd.
Phone: +44-0-1206-391509 Fax:+44-0-1206-395286
Unit 6, Causeway End, Station Road,
Lawford, Essex, CO11 1AA, England.
E-Mail: info@stalok.com   WEB: http://www.stalok.com
Check their WEB site for worldwide distributors list.

Navtec Corporation
Phone: 203-458-3163   Fax: 203-458-9291
351 New Whitfield Street Guilford, CT 06437-0388
E-Mail: navtec@navtec.net
WEB: http://www.navtec.net/home/index.cfm

COPPER MESH/SCREEN/STRAP

Newmar Corporation USA
Phone: 714-751-0488   Fax: 714-957-1621
P.O. Box 1306 Newport Beach, CA 92663
Factory: 2911 W. Garry Ave. Santa Ana, CA 92704
WEB: http://www.newmarpower.com

Newmar Corporation Europe
Contact: Hans Van Der Heijden
Phone: +31-35-603-2494   Fax: +31-35-603-2149
    --See also Marine SSB Radio Systems & Modems

DC COMPUTER POWER SUPPLY-NO RFI!

Computer Voltage Booster, Sam Ulbing, N4UAU
Phone: 352-375-3351
5200 NW 43rd St., Suite 102-177 Gainesville, Florida 32606
E-Mail: N4UAU@ARRL.net
WEB: http://user.gru.net/n4uau/kits/

HF RADIO E-MAIL FOR "IDI-YACHTS"®
HF MODEM TO RADIO DIN CABLES

BUX Comm Co.
115 Luenburg Drive Evington, Virginia 24550
http://www.packetradio.com/tnc2rad.htm

--See also Marine SSB Radio Systems & Modems

MARINE SSB RADIO SYSTEMS & MODEMS

California

*Baytronics South, Johnny Lindstrom
Phone: 310-915-1616   Fax: 310-915-1973
11315 Washington Place Los Angeles, CA 90066
http://www.baytronics.com

Downwind Marine, Chris or Linda
Phone: 619-224-2733   Fax: 619-224-7683
2804 Canon Street San Diego, CA 92106
http://www.downwindmarine.com

**Farallon Electronics, Eric Steinberg
Phone: 415-331-1924   Fax: 415-331-2063
2346 Mainship Way, Suite 101 Sausalito CA 94965
http://www.yachtwire.com

*H.F. Radio On Board, Don Melcher
Phone: 510-814-8888   Fax: 510-769-1573
1813 Clement Ave., #24 Alameda, CA 94501
http://www.hfradio.com

*Hi-Tek PC Solutions, David Reynolds
42880 Joshua Tree Court, Murieta, CA 92562
Phone: 909-461-8528   Fax: 909-461-8528
http://www.hitekpc.com

---

*= Authorized SCS PTC Dealer, ** = North American SCS PTC Distributor

*Johnson Hicks Marine, Joe Donatini
333 Lake Ave. #C, Santa Cruz, CA   95062
Phone: 831-475-3383   Fax: 831-475-1498
E-mail: jhme6@cs.com

*Long Beach Marine Electronics, Kevin Savord
6400 Marina Dr., #4 Long Beach, CA 90803
Phone: 562-594-8888   Fax: 562-799-1102
http://www.longbeachmarine.com

*Maritime Communications Inc., Ken Englert
766 Washington Blvd., Marina del Rey, CA 90292
Phone: 310-821-4958   Fax: 310-821-9591
E-mail: marcomm@aol.com

*Maritime Electronics of Sausalito, Galen Onizuka
300 Harbor Dr., Sausalito, CA 94965
Phone: 415-332-5086   Fax: 415-332-6344
http://www.maritimeelectronics.com

Maritime Electronics, Terence M. Boland
Phone: 800-582-1333, Santa Cruz CA USA
E-mail: MESCUSA@att.net

*Offshore Outfitters, Shea Weston
Phone: 619-225-5690   Fax: 619-509-2082
1273 Scott Street, Suite D, San Diego, CA 920016
http://www.offshoreoutfitters.com

*Voyager Marine Radio, Wade White
829 Harbor Island Drive, Newport Beach, CA 92660
Phone:760-365-0901   Fax: 760-285-9929
E-mail:captwade@adelphia.net

West Marine
Consult their store catalog for nationwide store listing.
http://www.westmarine.com

*= Authorized SCS PTC Dealer

Connecticut

*Custom Navigation, Steve Gill
633 Boston Post Rd., Westbrook, CT 06498
Phone: 860-399-5511   Fax: 860-399-5683
http://www.customnav.com

Landfall Navigation®, Capt. Henry Max
Phone: 203-487-0775   Fax: 203-487-0776
151 Harvard Avenue Stamford, CT 06902
http://www.landfallnav.com

Florida

ARC-Marine Inc., Ian Roberts
Phone: 954-630-0751, Ft. Lauderdale FL
http://www.arc-marine.com

Concord Electronics, Michael Robilio
Phone: 954-779-1100   Fax: 954-779-7090
2233 South Federal Hwy. Fort Lauderdale, FL 33316
http://www.concordelectronics.com

*DockSide Radio, Gary Jensen
Phone: 619-890-4533, Punta Gorda, FL
http://www.docksideradio.com

Gulfstream Marine Services, Carter Swartz
10720 72nd Street, Suite 305, Largo, FL 33777
Phone: 727-544-9660   Fax: 727-546-1979
http://www.gulfstreammarineservices.com

*MarineNet Wireless, John Heron
Phone: 561-747-5686,   Fax: 561-747-9357
17940 Loxahatchee River Road Jupiter, Florida 33458
http://www.marinenet.net

---

* = Authorized SCS PTC Dealer

*Mike's Electronics, Mike Spivak
Phone: 1-800-427-3066 954-491-7110, Fax: 954-491-7011
1001 NW 52 ST., Ft. Lauderdale, FL 33309
E-mail: mspivak@bellsouth.net

*Miller Marine, Al Meunier
Phone: 904-388-3690   Fax: 904-389-8555
4228 Lakeside Drive Jacksonville FL 32210
http://www.millermarine.com

*Sea Wiz Marine, Tom Dodamead
2250 Overseas Hwy, PO Box 501396 Marathon, FL 33050
Phone: 305-289-4044   Fax:305-289-3090
http://www.seawizmarine.com

*SeaTech Systems, Lou Iserhardt
1160 Serpentine Dr. South, St. Petersburg, FL 33705
Phone: 727-865-0159
http://www.sea-tech.com

Hawaii

*Navtech Marine Electronics, Ryan Haagensen
965 B North Nimitz Highway, Honolulu, HI 96817
Phone: 808-536-3700   Fax: 808-536-7656
http://www.navtechmarine.com

Maine

*Marine Computer Systems, Dan Piltch
Phone: 207-871-1575   Fax: 207-871-1834
58 Fore Street Portland, Maine 04101
http://www.marinecomputer.com

Midcoast Marine Electronics, Kevin Boughton
25 Oak Street, PO 669 Rockland, ME
Phone: 207-594-8277   Fax: 207-596-7248
http://www.midcoast.com

= Authorized SCS PTC Dealer

Michigan

*Off-Shore Marine, Craig Brumels
6883 4 Mile Rd. NE Ada, MI 49301
Phone: 616-890-1407   Fax: 619-954-9866
E-mail: scenano@earthlink.net

New Hampshire

*Navtronics, LLC, Maggie Deveau
131 Mirona Road Portsmouth, NH 03801
Phone: 603-436 2544   Fax: 603-436-2591
http://www.navtronics.com

New York

Innovative Marine Services, David Fontaine
Phone: 914-698-4959, Mamaroneck, NY
E-mail: ims.mail@verizon.net

*RadCom Technologies, Murray Cohen
509 Center Avenue Mamaroneck, NY 10543
Phone: 914-698-6800   Fax: 914-698-6801
E-mail: radcommarine@aol.com

Oregon

*Rodgers Marine Electronics, Marty Kirk
3445 NE Marine Drive Portland, Oregon 97211
Phone: 503-287-1101   Fax: 503-288-3745
http://www.rodgersmarine.com

Pennsylvania

*Marine Computer Systems, Tim Hasson
19 Walnut Ln., PO Box 262 Salford, PA 18957
Phone: 610-287-0703   Fax: 847-589-6550
http://www.marinecomputer.com

Rhode Island

*Custom Navigation, Steve Gill
1 Lagoon Road, Suite 5 Portsmouth, RI 02806
Phone: 401-683-6005   Fax: 401-683-6007
E-mail: sggill@compuserve.com

* = *Authorized SCS PTC Dealer*

Texas

*Sea Tech Systems™, Steve Bowden & Pamela House
PO Box 1352, Kemah, TX 77565
Phone: 800-444-2581, 281-334-1174, Fax: 281-334-3320
http://www.sea-tech.com

Washington, D.C.

*Cruising Services & Supplies, Dick Juppenlatz
2307 Huidekoper Place, NW Washington, DC 20007
Phone: 800-308-0739, 202-342-0191
E-mail: CruisingServices@aol.com

Washington State

Windward Communications, Chip Adams
Phone: 425-355-5176, Mukilteo, WA
E-mail: windward@wpfae.org

*Emerald City Marine, Ed Legard
1900 N. Northlake Way Suite 113, Seattle, WA 98103
Phone: 206-547-8171   Fax 206-547-3407
http://www.emeraldmarine.com

*The Offshore Store, Brian Rickard
3400 Stone Way Seattle, WA 98103
Phone: 206-632-3025   Fax: 206-632-0971
http://www.offshorestore.net

Australia

Bluewater Electronics, Sixten Lundgren
Phone: +61-7-4041-0333   Fax: +61-7-4051-3800
150a Sheridan Street Cairns QLD 4870 - Australia
http://www.ledanet.com

Navcom, Bob Stroud
Phone: +61-8-8981-1311, Darwin, Australia
E-mail: Bob.Stroud@navcom.com.au

= Authorized SCS PTC Dealer

HF RADIO E-MAIL FOR "IDI-YACHTS"®

PCA.CC, Marc Robinson,
Phone: +61-2-8902-0107, Sydney, Australia
E-mail: marc@pca.cc

Seabourne Electronics, Paul Weldon
Phone: +61-7-4771-4210, South Townsville, Australia
E-mail: seabourne@ozemail.com.au

British Virgin Islands

Cay Electronics Ltd., Rob Wassell
Phone: 284-494-2400, St John British Virgin Islands
E-mail: caybvi@candwbvi.net

Canada

*Durham Radio, Keith Carcasole,
Phone: 905-665-5466, Whitby ON, Canada
E-mail: info@durhamradio.com

*Les Produits Electroniques ELKEL, Dannis Rene
2575 Girard Trois-Rivières, QC G8Z 2M3 Canada
Phone: 866-383-5535   Fax: 819-378-0269
http://www.elkel.ca

*Naviclub, Pierre Begin or Guy Begin
LTEE   5054 rue St-Georges Levis, QC G6V 4P2   Canada
Phone: 418-835-9279   Fax: 418-835-6681
http://www.naviclub@naviclub.com

*Ocean Marine Outfitters, Dwight Hamilton
73 Railside Rd. Toronto, ON M3A 1B2 Canada
Phone: 416-444-0105   Fax: 416-444-8995
http://www.oceanmarine.on.ca

Oceanside Communication Systems, William Latter
Phone: 902-634-4430, Lunenburg NS, Canada
E-mail: oceanview1@ns.sympatico.ca

---

*= Authorized SCS PTC Dealer

150

*Service de Communications Morrissette Ltee, Luis Cortes
7075 Place Robert Joncas Ville St Laurent, QC H4M 2Z2
Phone: 514-956-7831   Fax: 514-956-7833
http://www.scmi.qc.ca

*Victoria Marine Electric Ltd., Larry Cole
31 Erie Street Victoria, B.C. V8V 1P8 Canada
Phone: 250-383-9731   Fax: 250-382-6153
http://www.victoriamarine.com

*Vancouver Marine Equipment
115-6753 Graybar Richmond, B.C. V6W 1H3 Canada
Phone: 800-863-8646
http://www.vancouvermarine.com

*White Squall Consulting Inc., Martin Dunsmuir
P.O. Box 2154 Sidney, B.C. V8L 3S6 Canada
Phone: 250-655-6653
E-mail: martin@whitesquallconsulting.com

Columbia

*Meltec S.A., Ana María Carvajal
Carrera 16 No. 34-14 Bogotá, Colombia
Phone: 57-1-2881161   Fax: 57-1-2887256
http://www.meltec.com.co

England

JG Technologies Ltd., John Grandshaw
Phone: 0845-458-9616, Weymouth, Dorset UK
E-mail: john@jgtech.co.uk

France

SUD Communications, Jean-Marc
Phone: 00-33-4-67509852, Montariol, France
E-mail: sudcom@wanadoo.fr

HF RADIO E-MAIL FOR "IDI-YACHTS"®

French Polynesia

*LSAC, Luc Callebaut
BP 380 210 PUNAAUIA, French Polynesia 98718
Phone: +689-20-45-87
E-mail:lucseawalker@bigfoot.com

Germany

Marineelectronic, Martin Reincke
Phone: +49-431-305-40-19,Kiel Germany
E-mail: reincke@boatcom.de

Holland

Shiptron, Hugo Baya
Phone: +31-228-317437, Enkhuizen Holland
E-mail: jb@shiptron.nl

Italy

Studio S.T.N., Marco Bonvino
Phone: 34-0-342-0714, Torino, Italy
E-mail: info@studiostn.com

Mexico

*Rob Ladner
Ocean Vista Residences Unit 409 Nuevo Vallarta, Nayarit
Phone:01-322-297-1557   VHF Channel 22 Radio Rob
E-mail: robk5rl@yahoo.com

New Zealand

Crystal Electronics, Bruce Lowrie
Phone: 64-9-5793726, Auckland, New Zealand
E-mail: sales@crystal.co.nz

*Sailboat Accessories, Leslie Egnot
PO Box 300-660 Albany, Auckland New Zealand
Phone:64-9-412-6949
E-mail: leslieegnot@compuserve.com

*= Authorized SCS PTC Dealer

Steelcon Electronics, Murray MacFadyen
Phone: 64-9-4384644, Whangarei, New Zealand
E-mail: murray@steelcon.co.nz

*Jacques Calvo
31 Raurenga Ave Epsom, Auckland 1003 New Zealand
Phone: +64-9-238-1316   E-mail: jcalvo@xtra.co.nz

South Africa

Reeves Marine, Bryn Reeves
Phone: 27-21-5111 430, Cape Town, South Africa
E-mail: brynr@rmarine.co.za

South East Asia

Brunei Bay Radio, Allan Riches
Phone: 673-8-723702, Brunei, Darussalam
E-mail: v8v2222@bruneibay.net

Switzerland

Ingenieurbüro für Telekommunikation, Robert Grisch
Phone: +41-62-771-23-55, Beinwil am See Switzerland
E-mail: rgrisch@seefunk.ch

The Netherlands

Dolstra Elektronika, Albert Dolstra
Phone: +31-511-465789, Bergum The Netherlands
E-mail: info@dolstra.nl

Kwadraad Sailors Solutions, Peter van der Wal
Phone: 0031-521-351588, Uffelte The Netherlands
E-mail: info@kwadraad.nl

Trinidad

*Navtech Electronics Limited, Aaron Hutchinson,
Coral Cove Marina, Western Main Road, Chaguaramas
Phone: 868-6341231
E-mail: navigationalelectron@tstt.net.tt

*= Authorized SCS PTC Dealer

MORSE CODE KEYERS

Milestone Technologies & Oak Hill Research
2460 S. Moline Way Aurora, CO 80014 USA
Phone: 303-752-3382   800-238-8205
E-mail: info@morsex.com
WEB: http://www.mtechnologies.com

POSITION REPORTING SOFTWARE

Pangolin Communications
Phone: 61- 407-923156
PO Box 14-778, Panmure, Auckland, New Zealand
YOTREPS
http://www.pangolin.co.nz/yotreps/32bit_reporter.php

PROPAGATION SOFTWARE

Pangolin Communications
Phone: 61- 407-923156
PO Box 14-778, Panmure, Auckland, New Zealand
"HF-PROP"
http://www.pangolin.co.nz/hf-prop.php

"ITSHF"
Freeware
http://www.airmail2000.com

RADIO FREQUENCY INTERFERENCE

RF Chokes/Ferrite Beads/Toroids

Amidon Associates, Inc.
Phone: 800-898-1883, 714-547-4494   Fax: 714-547-4433
1510 E. Edinger Avenue, Unit B Santa Ana CA 92705
http://www.amidon-inductive.com/

Digi-Key Corporation
Phone: 800-344-4539, 218-6816674   FAX: 218-681-3380
701 Brooks Avenue South, Thief River Falls, MN 56701
http://www.digikey.com

Fair-Rite Products Corp.
Phone: 914-895-2055   Fax: 914-895-2629
PO Box J, 1 Commercial Row Wallkill, NY 12589
http://www.fair-rite.com/

Intermark Corporation, Inc.
Phone: 718-392-5500, 800-426-4142
Fax: 718-392-7550
43-01 21st Street, Unit C10-B Long Island City, NY 11101
http://www.intermark-usa.com

Newark InOne Electronics
Phone: 800-4NEWARK, 773-784-5100
4801 N. Ravenswood Avenue Chicago, IL 60640-4496
http://www.newarkinone.com

Palomar
Phone: 760-747-3343   Fax: 760-747-3346
PO 462222 Escondido, CA 92046
http://www.palomar-engineers.com/

The Radio Works
Phone: 800-280-8327, 757-484-0140
PO Box 6159 Portsmouth, VA 23703
http://www.radioworks.com

The WireMan, Inc.
Phone: 864-895-4195   Fax: 864-895-5811
261 Pittman Road, Landrum, SC 29356
http://www.thewireman.com

--See also Marine SSB Radio Systems & Modems

T-4 Line Isolators

The Radio Works
Phone: 800-280-8327, 757-484-0140
PO Box 6159 Portsmouth, VA 23703
http://www.radioworks.com

Noise Filters-DC

RadioShack®
Phone: 800-THE-SHACK
http://www.radioshack.com

SATELLITE PHONE DATA COMPRESSION

XGate
Luis Soltero, Ph.D., MCS, Director of Software Development
Global Marine Networks, LLC
Phone: 865-379-8723   Fax: 865-681-5017
E-Mail: lsoltero@globalmarinenet.net
Web: http://www.globalmarinenet.net

SSB WHIP ANTENNAS

Shakespeare®
Composites & Electronics Division · Marine Products
Phone: 803-276-5504   Fax: 803-276-8940
19845 Highway 76, PO Box 733, Newberry, SC 29108
Galaxy Style Part #: 5390 17'6" HF/SSB Whip
Galaxy Style Part #: 5310-R 23' HF/SSB Whip
http://www.shakespeare-marine.com

USB TO SERIAL PORT CONVERTERS

BUX Comm Co.
115 Luenburg Drive Evington, Virginia 24550
http://www.packetradio.com/tnc2rad.htm
Part Number: USB2SC

GPS City®.com
Phone: 886-GPS-CITY, 702-990-5600 Fax: 702-990-5603
6 SunsetWay, Suite108 Henderson, NV 89014
http://www.gpscity.com   Part Number: 10310-6

RadioShack®
Phone: 800-THE-SHACK
http://www.radioshack.com   Part Number: 26-183

*Computer Discount Warehouse
StarTech USB to Serial Port Converter #:ICUSB232
WEB: http://www.cdw.com
Recommended by the Winlink development team.

–See also Marine SSB Radio Systems & Modems

WEATHER PRODUCT DOWNLOADS

OCENS, Weather Net™
Ocean and Coastal Environmental Sensing, Inc.
19655 First Avenue South, Suite 202 Seattle, WA 98148
Phone:800-746-1462, 206.878.8270   Fax: 206-878-8314
WEB: http://www.ocens.com/index.htm
E-mail: info@ocens.com

WEATHER FORECAST SERVICES

Buoyweather.com, Dan Martin
Customized weather forecasts for mariners.
WEB: http://www.buoyweather.com
E-Mail: Dan_Martin@buoyweather.com

The Caribbean Weather Center Ltd., David Jones
PO Box 3069, Road Town, Tortola, BVI
Phone: 1-284-494-7559   Fax: 1-284-494 5358
Email: weather@caribwx.com WEB: www.caribwx.com

Herb Hilgenberg, Southbound II
WEB: http://www3.sympatico.ca/hehilgen/vax498.htm
E-Mail: hehilgen@sympatico.ca

WEATHER RELATED SOFTWARE

Weather Training

Starpath School of Navigation
3050 NW 63rd Street Seattle, WA 98107, U.S.A.
Phone: 206-783-1414   Fax: 206-783-9209
WEB: http://www.starpath.com
For a free apparent to true wind converter go to:
http://www.starpath.com/freeware/true_wind.htm

GRIB WEATHER READERS

Xaxero Wind Plot
Xaxero Marine Software Engineering Ltd.
Phone: 64-9-412-7580   Fax: 64-9-412-7579
Auckland, New Zealand
WEB: http://www.xaxero.com   E-mail: xaxero@xaxero.com

RayTech 4.1
Raymarine Limited Corporate Headquarters
Phone: +44 (0) 23 9269 3611 Fax: +44 (0) 23 9269 4642
Anchorage Park
Portsmouth, Hampshire PO3 5TD United Kingdom

Raymarine, Inc. US Sales & Marketing
22 Cotton Road Unit D Nashua, New Hampshire 03063
Phone: 603-881-5200   Fax: 603-864-4756
http://www.raymarine.com

AirMail/SailMail GRIB Viewer
http://www.airmail2000.com or http://www.sailmail.com

WEATHER FAX SOFTWARE

Xaxero Weather Fax 2000 (Includes NAVTEX)
Xaxero Marine Software Engineering Ltd.
Auckland, New Zealand
Phone: 64-9-412-7580   Fax: 64-9-412-7579
Email: xaxero@xaxero.com WEB: http://www.xaxero.com

Distributor in USA:
Sea Tech Systems,™ Steve Bowden & Pamela House
PO Box 1352, Kemah, TX 77565
Phone: 800-444-2581, 281-334-1174, Fax: 281-334-3320
http://www.sea-tech.com

JVComm32
Eberhard Backeshoff
Obschwarzbach 40a 40822 Mettmann Germany
Email: feedback@jvcomm.de
WEB: http://www.jvcomm.de

Mscan Meteo Pro (Includes NAVTEX)
Mscan Meteo Fax
CombiTech
P.O. Box 8041, NL-4330EA Middelburg, Netherlands.
FAX: +31 118 601104
E-mail: combitech@mscan.com
WEB: http://www.mscan.com

AirMail Get Fax
http://www.airmail2000.com

WINDOWS SOFTWARE EMULATORS

http://www.macwindows.com

WINDOWS OPERATING SYSTEM UPDATES

Microsoft Corporation
Go to "Windows Update" at: http://www.microsoft.com

_____

_____

_____

_____

_____

_____

_____

_____

_____

_____

_____

_____

_____

_____

APPENDIX D
RESOURCES

HAM CONTACTS & INFO

AUSTRALIA
Wireless Institute of Australia [WIA]
Location: Suite 10, 229 Balaclava Rd., North Caulfield,
Victoria 3161 Address: P.O. Box 2175, Caulfield Junction,
Victoria 3125
Tel: +61 (3) 9528-5962 <Federal Office>, (8) 94099680
<VK6NE> Fax: +61 (3) 9523-8191 <Federal Office>
Email: wiafed@hotkey.net.au <Federal Office>,
ernest.hocking@aus.sun.com <VK1LK>
Web: http://www.wia.org.au
President: Ernest Hocking, VK1LK Secretary: Peter Naish, VK2BPN
IARU liaison: Neil Penfold, VK6NE Last updated: 12-Mar-2003

BAHAMAS
Bahamas Amateur Radio Society [BARS]
Address: P.O. Box SS-6004, Nassau, N.P.
President: Reinhart Pearson, C6ANO
Secretary & IARU liaison: Philip Dawkins, C6ACN
Last updated: 9-Mar-2003

BARBADOS
Amateur Radio Society of Barbados [ARSB]
Address: P.O. Box 814E, Bridgetown
Tel: +1 (809) 426-2502
President: Douglas Fredrick, 8P6BQ Secretary: John, 8P6FE Last
Last updated: 9-Mar-2003

HF RADIO E-MAIL FOR "IDI-YACHTS"®

BERMUDA
Radio Society of Bermuda [RSB]
Address: P.O. Box HM 275, Hamilton HM AX
Tel: +1 (441) 232-0292 <VP9IM>, 295-5881 <S. Dunkerley>, +1
(441) 295-5675 <Director Glen Cuoco, VP9ID>
Fax: +1 (441) 232-0293 <VP9IM>
Email: gcuoco@ibl.bm <Director Glen Cuoco, VP9ID>
Web: http://www.bermudashorts.bm/rsb
President: Rick Shirran, VE3NUZ/VP9
Secretary: John Stevens, VE3KXX/VP9
IARU liaison: Steve Dunkerley, VP9IM, P.O. Box HM 2215, Hamilton
HM JX Last updated: 9-Mar-2003

BRITISH VIRGIN ISLANDS
British Virgin Islands Radio League [BVIRL]
Address: P.O. Box 540, East End, Tortola
Tel: +1 (284) 494-4234 <VP2VI>, (284) 496-8992 <VP2VE> Email:
vp2ve@surfbvi.com <VP2VE>
Vice President: Lee Reisenweber, VP2VE
IARU liaison: Vice President Last updated: 25-Apr-2003

BRUNEI DARUSSALAM
Brunei Darussalam Amateur Radio Association [BDARA]
Address: Log Bag 73, MPC, BB3577, Negara Brunei Darussalam
Tel: +673 (8) 710867 <V85MH> Fax: +673 (2) 381169 <V85SK
President: Hj Hasnan bin Hj Shaari, V85MH
Secretary: Hj. Suhaili bin Hj Kawang, V85SK
IARU Liaison: President Last updated: 9-Mar-2003

CANADA
Radio Amateurs of Canada [RAC]
Address: 720 Belfast Road, Suite 217, Ottawa, Ontario K1G0Z5
Tel: +1 (613) 244-4367 <HQ>, (613) 225-3108 <VE3PU>
Fax: +1 (613) 244-4369 <HQ>, (613) 225-3818 <VE3PU>
Email: rachq@rac.ca <HQ>, ve3pu@rac.ca <VE3PU>
Web: http://www.rac.ca
President: William J. Gillis, VE1WG, Secretary: Dawn MacKay,
VE1MAK, General Manager: Deborah Norman, VA3RGM
IARU liaison: Ken Pulfer, VE3PU Last updated: Mar-2003

CAYMAN ISLANDS
Cayman Amateur Radio Society [CARS]
Address: P.O. Box 1029 GT, Grand Cayman
Tel: +1 (345) 945-4660 <ZF1DJ>
Fax: +1 (345) 945-4839 <ZF1DJ>
Email: darbyfam@candw.ky <ZF1DJ>, cqandy@candw.ky
<ZF1HQ>, aquadesi@candw.ky <ZF1EJ>
Web: http://cayman.com.ky/pub/radio/index.htm
President: John Darby, ZF1DJ Secretary: Andy Harding, ZF1HQ
IARU liaison: Andrew Eden, ZF1EJ
Last updated: 9-Mar-2003

COSTA RICA
Radio Club de Costa Rica [RCCR]
Address: P.O. Box 2412-1000, San Jose
Tel: +506 280-7855 <HQ>
Email: ti0rc@ti0rc.org <HQ>, earamirezz@hotmail.com <TI2CLP>,
caure@softhome.net <TI2CAU>, mgmoya@racsa.co.cr <TI3MGM>
Web: http://www.ti0rc.org
President: Alberto Ramirez, TI2CLP Secretary: Minor Moya,
TI3MGM IARU liaison: Carlos Urena, TI2CAU

CUBA
Federacion de Radioaficionados de Cuba [FRC]
Location: Paseo #611, entre 25 y 27, Plaza de la Revolucion,
Habana 10400
Address: P.O. Box 1, Habana 10100
Tel: +53 (7) 34811 & 302223 Fax: +53 (7) 335365
Email: frcuba@ip.etecsa.cu Web: http://frc.co.cu
President: Pedro Rodriguez, CO2RP
Secretary: Oscar Morales Jr., CO2OJ
IARU liaison: Vice President Francisco Hernandez, CO2HA Last
updated: 9-Mar-2003

HF RADIO E-MAIL FOR "IDI-YACHTS"®

DOMINICA
Dominica Amateur Radio Club [DARC]
Location: 69 Cork Street, Roseau
Address: P.O. Box 613, Roseau
Tel: +1 (767) 448-8533 <HQ> Fax: +1 (767) 448-7708 <HQ>
Email: j73z@hotmail.com
President: Joseph Raymond, J73RJ Secretary: Valda Woodman,
J73VW IARU liaison: Clement James, J73CI
Last updated: 9-Mar-2003

DOMINICAN REPUBLIC
Radio Club Dominicano [RCD]
Address: P.O. Box 1157, Santo Domingo
Tel: +1 (809) 533-2211
Email: vbaezr@hotmail.com <HI8VBR>
Web: http://www.radioclubdominicano.org
President: Hugo Ramon Sanchez, HI8VRS
Secretary: Victor Baez, HI8VBR
IARU liaison: William Read, HI8WA Last updated: 9-Mar-2003

FRANCE
Union Francaise des Radioamateurs [REF-Union]
Location: 32 Rue de Suede, F-37100 Tours
Address: P.O. Box 7429, F-37074 Tours Cedex 2
Tel: +33 (2) 4741-8873 <HQ> Fax: +33 (2) 4741-8888 <HQ>
Email: ref@ref-union.org <HQ>, f6ioc@free.fr <F6IOC>, f5gzj@ref-union.org <F5GZJ>
Web: http://www.ref-union.org
President: Jean Dumur, F5GZJ Secretary: Roger Lucas, F5MBK
IARU liaison: Betty Magnin, F6IOC
Last updated: 9-Mar-2003

FRENCH POLYNESIA
Club Oceanien de Radio et d'Astronomie [CORA]
Address: P.O. Box 5006, Pirae 98716, Tahiti
Tel: +689 436258/412525 <FO5EC>, 412923/425025 <FO4NR>
Fax: +689 412723 <FO4NR>
President: Charles Trondle, FO5BL
Sec: Alain Portal, FO5EC IARU liaison: Richard Slavov, FO4NR

GERMANY

Deutscher Amateur Radio Club [DARC]
Location: Lindenallee 4 Address: D-34225 Baunatal
Tel: +49 (561) 949880 <HQ>, (2203) 21993 <DL9KCX>, (4502) 777334 <Hans Berg>
Fax: +49 (561) 9498850 <HQ>, (4502) 777332 <DJ6TJ>
Email: darchq@t-online.de <HQ>, dl9kcx@darc.de <DL9KCX>, dj6tj@t-online.de <DJ6TJ>
Web: http://www.darc.de
President: Jochen Hindrichs, DL9KCX
Secretary: Bernd W. Haefner, DB4DL
IARU liaison: Hans Berg, DJ6TJ Last updated: 27-May-2003

GRENADA

Grenada Amateur Radio Club [GARC]
Address: P.O. Box 737, St. George's
Tel: +1 (809) 443-2662 <J39DF>
President: John Phillip, J39CR
Secretary: Jerry Aberdeen, J39DF
IARU liaison: Secretary Last updated: 9-Mar-2003

GUATEMALA

Club de Radioaficionados de Guatemala [CRAG]
Location: Local 117, 3rd Floor, Centro Comercial Super Centro Molino, Calzada Roosevelt, Km. 15,Zona 11, G.C.
Address: P.O. Box 115, Guatemala City 01901
Tel: +502 437-2027 <HQ>, 431-5915 <TG9AGD>, 432-1313 <TG9CC>
Fax: +502 437-2027 <HQ>, 439-5262 <TG9CC>
Email: crag@gua.net <HQ>, tg9agd@itelgua.com <TG9AGD>
Web: http://www.crag.8m.com
President: Marco Tulio Gudiel Dardon, TG9AGD
Secretary: Dany Eduardo Ardon Moreles, TG9AMD
IARU liaison: President Last updated: 9-Mar-2003

HF RADIO E-MAIL FOR "IDI-YACHTS"®

ITALY

Associazione Radioamatori Italiani [ARI]
Address: Via Scarlatti 31, I-20124 Milano
Tel: +39 (2) 6692192 <HQ>, +39 (10) 564975 <I1BYH>, +39 (2)
95321201 <I2MQP> Fax: +39 (2) 66714809 <HQ>
Email: ari@micronet.it <HQ>, i2mqp@ari.it <I2MQP>
Web: http://www.ari.it
President: Alessio Ortona, I1BYH Secretary: Daniele Taliani,
IV3TDM IARU liaison: Mario Ambrosi, I2MQP
Last updated: 9-Mar-2003

SOUTH AFRICA

South African Radio League [SARL]
Location: Sender Technology Park, Octave Street, Honeydew,
Johannesburg
Address: P.O. Box 1721, Strubensvallei 1735
Tel: +27 (11) 675-2393 <HQ>, (31) 765-6334 <ZS5AKV>
Fax: +27 (11) 675-2793 <HQ>, (31) 765-6456 <ZS5AKV>
Email: admin@sarl.org.za Web: http://www.sarl.org.za
President: Sid Tyler, ZS6AYC Office Administrator: Marlette
Kroukamp IARU liaison: Hans van de Groenendaal, ZS5AKV Last
updated: 9-Mar-2003

SWITZERLAND

Union Schweizerischer Kurzwellen-Amateure [USKA]
Address: P.O. Box 238, CH-4805 Brittnau
Tel: +41 (62) 7528284 <HQ>, (81) 7504115 <HB9AAQ>, (52)
3438884 <HB9JNS>, (62) 8220629 <HB9AHL (H)>, (31) 324 78 31
<HB9AHL (W)>
Fax: +41 (62) 7528289 <HQ>, (62) 8234623 <HB9AHL>
Email: hq@uska.ch <HQ>, sekr@uska.ch <HB9JNS>,
hb9ahl@uska.ch <HB9AHL> Web: http://www.uska.ch
President: Fred Tinner, HB9AAQ
Secretary: Barbara Schleutermann, HB9JNS
IARU liaison: Willy Ruesch, HB9AHL, Bahnhofstrasse 26, CH-5000
Aarau Last updated: 28-Apr-2003

TRINIDAD & TOBAGO
Trinidad and Tobago Amateur Radio Society [TTARS]
Address: P.O. Box 1167, Port of Spain
Tel: +868 633-2725 <9Z4CP>, 632-2798 <9Y4KLF>, +868 663-3423 <9Y4MM>
Email: info@ttars.org <HQ>, ka2mmf@yahoo.com <9Y4MM>, 9Z4CP@rave-tt.net <9Z4CP>
Web: ttars.org
President: Eric Mackie, 9Z4CP Secretary: Klevin Lee Foon, 9Y4KLF
IARU liaison: Lemuel Jeffers, 9Y4MM Last updated: 6-Jun-2003

TURKS & CAICOS ISLANDS Turks and Caicos Amateur Radio
Society [TACARS]
Address: P.O. Box 218, Providenciales, Turks & Caicos Island
Tel: +649 946-4436 <VP5JM>, 946-2216 <VP5FEB>
Fax: +649 941-3824 <VP5JM>
Email: jody@tciway.tc <VP5JM>
President: Frederick Braithwaite, VP5FEB Secretary: Jody
Millspaugh, VP5JM IARU liaison: Secretary Last updated: Mar-2003

UNITED STATES OF AMERICA
American Radio Relay League [ARRL]
Address: 225 Main Street, Newington, CT 06111-1494
Tel: +1 (860) 594-0200 <HQ>
Fax: +1 (860) 594-0259 <HQ>
Email: hq@arrl.org <HQ>, w5jbp@arrl.org <W5JBP>, dsumner@arrl.org <K1ZZ>, w6rod@arrl.org <W6ROD>
Web: http://www.arrl.org
President: Jim D. Haynie, W5JBP Secretary: David Sumner, K1ZZ
IARU liaison: Rodney Stafford, W6ROD
Last updated: 9-Mar-2003

W5YI
P. O. Box 565101, Dallas, Texas 75356
2000 E. Randol Mill Road, Suite #608-A, Arlington, TX 76011
Phone: 817-274-0400, 800-669-9594 FAX: 817-548-9594
WEB: http://www.w5yi.org Email: w5yi@w5yi.org

HF RADIO E-MAIL FOR "IDI-YACHTS"®

UNITED KINGDOM
Radio Society of Great Britain [RSGB]
Address: Lambda House, Cranborne Road., Potters Bar, Herts.
EN6 3JE
Tel: +44 (1707) 659015 <HQ>, (1707) 659015 <G0TWW
Fax: +44 (1707) 645105 <HQ>
Email: gm.dept@rsgb.org.uk
Web: http://www.rsgb.org
President: Dr. Bob Whelan, G3PJT
Secretary and General Manager: Peter Kirby, G0TWW
IARU liaison: General Manager Last updated: 9-Mar-2003
–For more HAM resources see the "Idi-Yacht" CD ROM.

HAM STUDY COURSES

Gordon West Radio School
2414 College Dr., Costa Mesa, CA, USA 92626
Phone: 714-549-5000   FAX: 714-434-0666
WEB: http://www.hamnet.net

MARINE SSB LICENSES

Australia
Australian Communications Authority
Central Office - Canberra
Purple Building, Benjamin Offices Belconnen ACT
Postal Address: PO Box 78 BELCONNEN ACT 2616
Phone: 02 6219 5555   Fax: 02 6219 5353

Central Office - Melbourne
13th Floor, 200 Queen Street Melbourne VIC
Postal Address: PO Box 13112 Law Courts Melbourne
VIC 8010
Phone: 03 9963 6800   Fax: 03 9963 6899

Canada
Atlantic Spectrum Regional Office
1045 Main Street 4th Floor, Unit 103 Moncton, N.B.
E1C 1H1
Phone: 506-851-6527   Fax: 506-851-7444

Quebec Regional Office
7th Floor 5 Place Ville-Marie, Montreal, Que. H3B 2G2
Phone:514-496-1797, 888-237-3037 Fax: 514-283-5157

Ontario Regional Office
4th Floor 151 Yonge St. Toronto, Ont. M5C 2W7
Phone: 416-973-5000   Fax: 416-973-6272
Prairie & Northern Region
4th Floor 400 St. Mary Avenue Winnipeg, Man. R3C 4K5
Phone: 204-983-5851   Fax: 204-983-3182
Pacific Regional Office
Room 2000, Library Square 300 West Georgia Street
Vancouver, B.C. V6B 6E1
Phone: 604-666-5000   Fax: 604-666-9698
WEB: http://strategis.ic.gc.ca/engdoc/main.html

United Kingdom
Requirements: Ships Radio License & Marine Radio
Operator's Certificate
Contact: Radio Licensing Centre
PO Box 885 Bristol, UK BS99 5LG
Ships Licenses
Phone: 0870-243-4433

USA
Federal Communications Commission (FCC)
Ship Radio Station License & Restricted Radio Telephone Operator
Permit–Universal Licensing System
1270 Fairfield Rd., Gettysburg, PA 17325-7245
Phone: Forms-800-418-FORMS   FEES:888-225-5322
WEB: http://www.wireless.fcc.gov

–See "Idi-Yacht" CD ROM for forms and information.

NWS WEATHER PRODUCTS

For questions or comments on the National Weather Service's marine weather program contact:
National Weather Service
Marine Program Leader W/OS21
1325 East West Highway
Silver Spring, MD 20910

General Inquiries
Brian LaMarre
Phone: 301-713-1677 x108   Fax: 301-713-1520
brian.lamarre@noaa.gov

Coastal Weather, Great Lakes, Ice
Wayne Weeks
Phone: 301-713-1677 x129   Fax: 301-713-1520
wayne.weeks@noaa.gov

Hurricanes, Tropical Storms
Scott Kiser
Phone: 301-713-1677 x121   Fax: 301-713-1520
scott.kiser@noaa.gov

Hurricanes, Tropical Storms, Coastal Flooding, Rip Currents Tim Schott
Phone: 301-713-1677 x122   Fax: 301-713-1520
timothy.schott@noaa.gov

GMDSS, MAROB, SafetyNet,NAVTEX, Radiofax, & Tsunami
Tim Rulon
Phone: 301-713-1677 x128   Fax: 301-713-1520
timothy.rulon@noaa.gov   marine.weather@noaa.gov
http://www.nws.noaa.gov/om/marine/home.htm

-Tim's website Includes an exhaustive listing of broadcast schedules-

APPENDIX D - RESOURCES

Observations, Tides, SST, Gulfstream
Richard May Phone: 301-713-1677 x127 Fax: 301-713-1520
richard.may@noaa.gov

For questions on the National Weather Service's highseas or offshore marine forecasts (except offshore forecasts in the Gulf of Mexico and Tropical Atlantic) of an operational nature contact:

David Feit, W/NP41 National Weather Service
Ocean Prediction Center (formally the Marine Prediction Center)
5200 Auth Road Camp Springs, MD 20746
Phone: 301-763-8441, 301-763-8000 x7401
Phone: 301-763-8592   Fax: 301-763-8085
david.feit@noaa.gov
http://www.mpc.ncep.noaa.gov/

For questions on the National Weather Service's tropical marine, hurricane and offshore forecasts in the Gulf of Mexico and Tropical Atlantic, of an operational nature contact:
Christopher A. Burr, Chief TAFB
National Weather Service, Tropical Prediction Center
11691 Southwest 17th St. Miami, FL 33165-2149
Phone: 305-229-4430, 305-229-4425 (24hr)
Fax: 305-553-1264
Christopher.A.Burr@noaa.gov   http://www.nhc.noaa.gov/

For questions or comments on U.S. Coast Guard communications of a general nature contact:
Commandant (G-SCT-2)
U.S. Coast Guard
Washington, D.C. 20593-0001
Phone: 202-267-2860   Fax:202-267-4106
cgcomms@comdt.uscg.mil
http://www.navcen.uscg.gov/marcomms/

HF RADIO E-MAIL FOR "IDI-YACHTS"®

For questions relating to operational USCG broadcasts, contact the relevant USCG communications station:
(Atlantic)
U.S. Coast Guard, Commander CAMSLANT
4720 Milepost Rd. Chesapeake, VA 23322-2598
Phone: 800-742-8519, 757-421-6240, 757-421-6268 (24 Hr)
Fax: 757-421-6255 LRitter@camslant.uscg.mil
 http://www.uscg.mil/lantarea/camslant/index.htm

(Pacific)
U.S. Coast Guard
Commander CAMSPAC
17000 Sir Francis Drake Blvd. P.O. Box 560
Pt. Reyes Station, CA 94956-0560
Phone: 877-662-4636, 415-669-2047 Fax: 415-669-2096
ddermanelian@d11.uscg.mil
http://www.uscg.mil/pacarea/camspac/menu.html

(Alaska)
U.S. Coast Guard
Commander COMMSTA Kodiak
P.O. Box 190017
Kodiak, AK 99619-0017
Phone: 907-487-5426, 24 HR 907-487-5778
Fax: 907-487-5517

For operational questions relating to the radiofax broadcast from Honolulu, HI contact:
(Hawaii - radiofax only)
Jay Delcano W/PR11X1
National Weather Service
Pacific Region Communications Manager
737 Bishop St.
Honolulu, HI 96813-3213
Phone: 808-532-6427   Fax: 808-532-5569
jay.delcano@noaa.gov

For operational questions relating to major systems outages affecting multiple NWS products contact: *Please be as specific with your question as possible and provide such information as system affected, product name, web address, etc.*
Systems Operations Center, National Weather Service
1325 East West Highway
Silver Spring, MD 20910
Phone: 301-713-0902   Fax: 301-587-1773

For questions on the NWS Tsunami Warning Program, contact the appropriate Tsunami Warning Center.
West Coast and Alaska Tsunami Warning Center (WC/ATWC)
910 South Felton St. Palmer, AK 99645
Paul Whitmore
Phone: 907-745-4212   Fax: 907-745-6071
Paul.Whitmore@noaa.gov
http://wcatwc.arh.noaa.gov/

Pacific Tsunami Warning Center (PTWC)
91-270 Fort Weaver Rd. Ewa Beach, HI 96706-2928
Charles McCreery
Phone: 808-689-8207 x301 Fax: 808-689-4543
charles.mccreery@noaa.gov
http://www.nws.noaa.gov/pr/ptwc/index.htm

For tide and tidal current predictions, real time, and historic information contact:
Tom Kendrick, Todd Ehret
NOAA, National Ocean Service, OPSD, User Services, N/OPS3
Attn: Tidal Predictions
1305 East-West Highway Silver Spring, MD 20910-3281
Phone: 301-713-2815   Fax: 301-713-4500
tide.predictions@noaa.gov
http://co-ops.nos.noaa.gov/

HF RADIO E-MAIL FOR "IDI-YACHTS"®

For questions on International Ice Patrol Products and Services
Commander International Ice Patrol
1082 Shennecossett Rd. Groton, CT 06340
Phone: 860-441-2631   Fax: 860-441-2773
iipcomms@rdc.uscg.mil
http://www.uscg.mil/lantarea/iip/home.html

For questions on National Ice Center Products and Services contact:
National Ice Center, Federal Building #4
4251 Suitland Rd. Washington D.C. 20395
Phone: 301-457-5303 x 236   http://www.natice.noaa.gov

For questions on Alaskan Ice and SST Products Contact:
Russel Page, National Weather Service
6930 Sandlake Rd. Anchorage, AK 99502-1845
Phone: 907-266-5113   Fax: 907-266-5188
http://www.arh.noaa.gov/

For questions on U.S. Navy meteorological programs contact:
Command Duty Officer, NAVLANTMETOCCEN
9141 3rd Ave. Norfolk, VA 23511
Phone: 757-444-4044
cdo@nlmoc.navy.mil
https://www.nlmoc.navy.mil/home.html

For questions of an operational nature relating to near shore and coastal forecasts in the US, contact the local National Weather Service Forecast Office. Numbers for local forecast offices may be found in the telephone directory white/blue pages under "United States Government"; "Commerce Department"; "National Weather Service".

APPENDIX E
GLOSSARY

Amateur Bands--The frequencies between 1.8 MHz to 29.7 MHz set aside for amateur radio operators (HAMs).

Amateur Packet Radio--Communications over HAM radio between two computers. Packet networks use relays and stations that act as bulletin boards for message storage, retrieval and forwarding.

Amperage--The strength of a current of electricity expressed and measured in amperes.

Amplitude--The height of a radio transmission or sound wave's loudness.

Amplitude Modulation--The addition of information to a RF carrier by increasing and decreasing amplitude. These are low efficiency types of radio transmissions, which are used for AM radio stations with 100 percent carrier inserted.

AMTOR--Amateur Radio Over Radio Teletype. A specialized type of RTTY.

Analog--Refers to signals that can represent an infinite range of numbers, as opposed to digital which can only be distinct whole numbers. Analogue data often comes from measurements, like a sine wave. The sound a modem makes over the phone is analog since it can be any of a number of different frequencies.

Antenna--Any structure or device used to collect or radiate electromagnetic waves

Airmail--HF radio E-mail software developed by Jim Corenman.

ARQ—Automatic Repeat reQuest. The HF modem notices errors in data received and automatically requests the other station to repeat the transmission.

Asynchronous Communication--Not synchronized; that is, not occurring at predetermined or regular intervals. The term asynchronous is usually used to describe communications in which data can be transmitted intermittently rather than in a steady stream. Most communications between computers and devices are asynchronous.

Aurora-- A faint visual phenomenon associated with geomagnetic activity, which occurs mainly in the high-latitude night sky. Typical auroras are 100 to 250 Km above the ground.

Baud--Baud in slow speed transmissions indicates the number of bits per second that are transmitted. For example, 300 baud means that 300 bits are transmitted each second. Assuming asynchronous communication, which requires 10 bits per character, this translates to 30 characters per second (cps). For slow rates (below 1,200 baud), you can divide the baud by 10 to see how many characters per second are sent.

Baud Rate--A measure of the speed of serial communication using a modem roughly equivalent to bits per second. A rate of 300 baud is about 30 characters per second.

Bits Per Second--bps. A standard measurement of data transmission speeds. How fast the modem can transmit and receive data. At slow rates, modems are measured in terms of baud rates. At higher speeds, modems are measured in terms of bits per second (bps). Modems can achieve even higher data transfer rates by compressing the data.

Byte--A unit of storage capable of holding a single character. On almost all modem computers, a byte is equal to 8 bits.

Capacitor--An electronic component that removes or quiets noise. Akin to putting your hand over a ringing bell.

Carrier Signal-- A frequency in a communications channel that is modulated to carry analog or digital signal information. For example, an FM radio transmitter modulates the frequency of a carrier signal and the receiver processes the carrier signal to extract the analog information.

Center Frequency--The midpoint of the Mark and Space Signal in a Frequency Shift Keying (FSK) mode.

COM Port--Abbreviation for **C**omponent **O**bject **M**odel. An interface on a computer where you can connect a device such as your HF radio modem. Personal computers have various types of ports for connecting modems, printers, mice, and other peripheral devices.

Counterpoise—Also known as a ground plane. Composed of copper mesh and/or copper strap it provides a trampoline effect for radio waves to send them soaring into space.

Continuity--Completeness of a circuit.

Coupler--Also known as an HF radio tuner--can be either automatic or manual.

Dial Frequency--For HF radio E-mail transmission this is the frequency that is entered into the radio.

DIN Plug--Short for Deutch International Standard.

DSP--Digital Signal Processing. High quality compression at low bit rates.

Doubling--Two stations transmitting at the same time on the same frequency. When two HF stations transmit simultaneously, all that is heard is goobledegook!

Duplex Frequency--Transmission is on one frequency and receive is on another frequency.

E-mail--Electronic mail. Messages that are sent to individual people. You choose who to send the message to and only that person receives the message.

E-mail Ready--A Marine SSB radio that is capable of transmitting at full power for one or two minutes. Also known as 100% duty cycle. *This does not mean that you can plug a computer into the radio directly and send and receive E-mail without an HF radio modem!* A rather misleading marketing term. It also does not imply that you should transmit on an E-mail system at full power.

Error Correction--The ability of a modem to notice errors in transmission, and to resend incorrect data.

HF RADIO E-MAIL FOR "IDI-YACHTS"®

Frequency--The number of polarity alternations per second measured in Hertz, whereas kilohertz (kHz) equals a thousand Hertz and Megahertz (MHz) equals a million Hertz. It's those numbers that you dial into your radio!

FEC--Forward Error Correcting. Sometimes called Mode B. The sending station transmits each letter twice. The receiving station does not have the ability to request a repeat of the data as in ARQ.

Ferrite Choke--See RF choke.

Free Signal-- Use of a dedicated HF radio for each frequency listed for an HF radio E-mail provider.

Frequency Scanning-- Use of one HF radio to scan several frequencies by an HF radio E-mail provider.

FSK--Short for Frequency Shift Keying. A modulation technique used by modems in which two different frequencies in the carrier signal are used to represent the binary states of 0 and 1. Using FSK, a modem converts the binary data from a computer into a binary form in which logic 1 is represented by an analog waveform at a specific frequency and logic 0 is represented by a wave at a different specific frequency.

Geomagnetic Storm-- A worldwide disturbance of the earth's magnetic field, distinct from regular diurnal variations. Can negatively affect HF radio propagation.

GRIB Weather Files--GRIded Binary data files (GRIB) are output files generated by computer forecasting models. They are tremendously more compact than regular weather charts and because of their size are very well suited for download via wireless means. NOAA GRIB files are the best ones for marine forecasts. GRIB weather files can be pure computer model data or data that have been modified by forecasters.

GMT--Greenwich Mean Time. By international agreement, the local time at the prime meridian, which passes through Greenwich, England. Therefore, it is also known as Greenwich Mean Time, or Universal Coordinated Time (UTC) or Zulu.

Groundplane—Composed of copper mesh and/or copper strap. It produces a trampoline effect for radio waves to send them soaring into space.

G-TOR—(Golay -TOR) is an FSK mode that offers a fast transfer rate compared to Pactor. It incorporates a data inter-leaving system that assists in minimizing the effects of atmospheric noise and has the ability to fix garbled data. G-tor tries to perform all transmissions at 300 baud but drops to 200 baud if difficulties are encountered and finally to 100 baud. (This protocol brought back those good photos of Saturn and Jupiter from the Voyager space shots. It was created by M. Golay and now adapted for ham radio use.)

HAM Radio--Also called Amateur radio. HF radio communication in a range of frequencies from just above the AM broadcast band (1.6 MHz) to the microwave region, at several hundred gigahertz. A license is required to transmit on these frequencies. There are hundreds of thousands of amateur radio operators in the U.S. and millions around the world. Ham radio can be useful in providing communications during emergencies when other services such as telephones, television or the Internet fail.

Handshaking--The process by which two modems initiate communications. Handshaking begins when one modem (you) sends a message to another modem (the service provider) indicating that it wants to establish a communications channel.

Hertz (Hz)--A measure of frequency, which is one cycle per second.

HF--High Frequency. Frequencies in the 3 to 30 MHz ranges.

HTML--Short for **H**yper**T**ext **M**arkup **L**anguage, the language used to create documents on the World Wide Web.

ITU--International Telecommunications Union, based in Geneva, Switzerland.

JB3--The emission type designator for transmission on Upper Side Band (USB).

HF RADIO E-MAIL FOR "IDI-YACHTS"®

LSB-- The Lower Sideband of a carrier frequency. It is a type of HF radio reception that demodulates AM signals by processing that portion of the received signal below the transmitter's carrier frequency. Ok well you wanted to know!

Line Isolator--A device that has five RF chokes inside a tube. It is installed in-between the HF radio and the radio tuner--as close to the radio tuner as possible. Its purpose is to squelch Radio Frequency Interference (RFI).

Mark--Traditionally the higher of the two transmitted signals in a Frequency Shift Keying (FSK) mode.

MF--Medium Frequencies. Frequencies from 300 kHz to 3 MHz.

Modem--Short for MOdulator-DEModulator. A modem is a device or program that enables a computer to transmit data. Computer information is stored digitally, whereas information transmitted over the HF radio is transmitted in the form of analogue waves. A modem converts between these two forms.

Modulate--To blend data into a carrier signal. At the receiving side, a device demodulates the signals by separating the constant carrier signals from the variable data signals. For example, radio uses two types of modulation - amplitude modulation (AM) and frequency modulation (FM) - to mix audio signals with an AM or FM carrier signal. A modem modulates data by converting it to audible tones that can be transmitted and demodulates received signals to get the data.

Modulation--The varying of amplitude, frequency, or phase of a carrier signal.

Morse Code--The first form of digital communications. Developed by Samuel Morse who wanted to keep in touch with his family when he was traveling.

Noise--In HF Radio, this is interference or static that destroys the integrity of received signals. Noise can come from a variety of sources, including radio waves, nearby electrical wires, lightning, inverters, battery chargers, wind generators, refrigerators and bad connections.

Ohm--A unit of measurement used to measure resistance to electrical current.

Ohms Law--A mathematical equation that shows the relationship between electric voltage, current and resistance. Ohm's Law was named after Bavarian mathematician and physicist George Ohm. Generally, Ohm's Law is only applied to DC circuits and not AC circuits.

Pactor--A Frequency Shift Keying mode. It is a standard on HF radio moderns. Designed with a combination of packet and AMTOR techniques. It is the most popular ARQ digital mode on amateur HF today.

Packet--HAM radio operating mode. Uses the complete ASCII character set which permits both upper and lowercase characters in a transmission.

PC--An abbreviation for **P**ersonal **C**omputer. Can also be used to mean Politically Correct.

PMBO--A Winlink 2000 Participating Mailbox Operator. PMBOs communicate with each other through the CMBO in a "star" network configuration via the Internet and with the end-users and other MBOs over radio.
Port--On the water, it's a place where one anchors. In a computer it is an interface or a connection where you plug equipment into.

Private Coast Station--An HF radio station that provides services to members of an association.

Propagation—The ability to transmit and receive clearly. Effected by the sun, surrounding electrical noise, atmospheric conditions, frequency selected, and time of day.

Public Coast Station--Commercial Marine SSB service provider.

QTH--A HAM abbreviation that means your Location.

RAM--An acronym for **R**andom **A**ccess **M**emory. RAM is the most common type of memory found in computers and printers. Think of RAM as a shopping cart. The larger your shopping cart, the fewer trips you'll have to make to get all of your groceries. The more RAM you have the faster your programs open and work.

RF--Radio Frequency. Higher than humans are capable of hearing.

RF Chokes--Devices that are primarily intended to "choke" off alternating currents, including RF from DC supply lines.

RFI—Radio Frequency Interference--see noise.

RS232 Port--A standard interface for connecting external modems to computers.

RTTY—"Radio Teletype" is a FSK mode that has been in use longer than any other digital mode (except for Morse code). RTTY is a very simple technique which uses a five-bit code to represent all the letters of the alphabet, the numbers, some punctuation and some control characters. There is no error correction provided in RTTY; noise and interference can have a seriously detrimental effect. Despite it's relative disadvantages, RTTY is still popular with diehard HAM operators.

Serial Port--The interface located in the back of your computer where you can plug in devices such as your HF radio modem. A port, or interface, that can be used for serial communication, in which only 1 bit is transmitted at a time. A serial port is a general-purpose interface that can be used for almost any type of device, including modems, mice, and printers.

Simplex Frequency--Transmit and receive are done on the same frequency. The majority of Marine SSB frequencies are simplex.

SITOR—An abbreviation for SImplex Teletype Over Radio.
A vessel equipped with SITOR is capable of automatically transmitting and receiving type written documents.

Solar Flares--is defined as an enormous explosion which is observed as a sudden, rapid, and intense variation in brightness in the solar atmosphere. It is believed to result from the sudden release of energy stored in the magnetic fields that thread the solar corona in active regions around sunspots involving sudden bursts of particle acceleration, plasma heating, and bulk mass motion. The Earth's upper atmosphere becomes more ionized and expands. Long distance radio signals can be disrupted by the resulting change in the Earth's ionosphere.

Solar Flare Index (SFI)--Classification of the severity of solar flares.

Space--Traditionally the lower of the two transmitted signals in a Frequency Shift Keying (FSK) mode.

SPAM--Telemarketing over the Internet where you are sent unwanted, unwelcome junk mail. To avoid getting spammed, never use your HF radio E-mail address to fill out forms on the Internet!

SSB--Single Sideband. A mode where the carrier and one sideband of the AM mode has been suppressed. Whether using USB (upper sideband) or LSB (lower sideband) more of the transmitter's signal is focused in the sideband used as compared to AM. SSB is the phone mode of choice for Amateurs on the HF bands.

Sunspots--Cooler (and thus darker) regions on the sun where the magnetic field loops up out of the solar surface. Affects HF radio propagation.

SWR--Standing Wave Ratio. The lower the SWR the better the match between the antenna and the transmitter. Ideally the SWR should be below 3:1. With a high SWR much of the transmitted signal is reflected back down the transmission line to the radio and not up to space. With a high SWR the radio will reduce it's transmitted or forward power to protect itself from damage. High SWR generally means there is a problem with the antenna.

TCP/IP--Abbreviation for **T**ransmission **C**ontrol **P**rotocol/**I**nternet **P**rotocol. The suite of communications protocols used to connect hosts on the Internet.

Toroid--see RF Chokes.

Transceiver--Radio equipment that transmits and receives.

Tuner--Equipment whose job it is to match the frequency with the antenna length. Can be manual or automatic.

USB--Universal Serial Bus. An external bus standard that supports data transfer rates of 12 Mbps. It is expected to completely replace serial and parallel ports.

HF RADIO E-MAIL FOR "IDI-YACHTS"®

USB--Upper Sideband of a carrier frequency in HF radio transmissions.

UTC—Universal Coordinated Time. The same as Greenwich Mean Time or Zulu.

Winlink 2000--HAM radio HF radio E-mail service provider.

WL2K-- Winlink 2000. The connecting stations for the HAM HF radio E-mail system.

Zulu--Another term for Greenwich Mean Time or UTC.

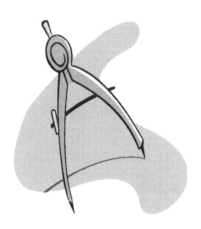

INDEX

SUPPLEMENTAL "IDI-YACHT"
CD ROM

INDEX

ACKNOWLEDGMENTS & CREDITS
ELECTRONIC NOISE
FTP MAIL INFO
GMDSS INFORMATION
GRIB WX READERS
HAM CONTACTS
HAM DIGITAL MODES
HF DIGITAL MODE SOUNDS
HF MODEM DIN PLUGS
HF RADIO INSTALLATION INFO
HF RADIO TRBLSHOOT
INSTALL FIRST
MARITIME NETS
MODEM OFF/ON SWITCH
PHONE CALLS MARINE SSB
POSITION RPT SOFTWARE
PROPAGATION ARTICLES
PROPAGATION SOFTWARE
PROVIDER SOFTWARE
REMOTE RADIO CONTROL
SCS PTC MODEM DEALERS
SCS MODEM SOFTWARE
SHIP STATION LICENSES
SOLDERING ARTICLES
WX BROADCAST PRODUCTS
WX FX SOFTWARE/SHAREWARE
WX SATELLITES SOFTWARE

OTHER BOOKS BY CAPTAIN MARTI

Learn how to use your Marine SSB radio the easy way! Marine SSB Radio For "Idi-Yachts" will help you get up to

speed on how to use your Marine SSB radio. The book is written in plain language we can all understand. It includes a removable "Quick Reference Guide" with hailing and working frequencies, weather & traffic Nets, voice and weather fax frequencies. A must have for newbees!

Available at Amazon.com, Bluewater Books, Landfall Navigation, West Marine and all fine bookstores.

About The Author

Captain Marti lives aboard and solos her 31' Allmand sailboat, *The Other Woman*. She has been sailing the Bahamas and Florida waters since 1990 and has been a HAM radio operator since 1997. Marti is a reporting station for the Hurricane Watch Net, a member of the Waterway Radio and Cruising Club, the Seven Seas Cruising Association and the American Radio Relay League. She is an Advanced Registered Nurse Practitioner, a licensed captain and currently resides in Boot Key Harbor, Marathon, in the Florida Keys.

Visit her on-line at:

http://www.idiyachts.com